OUR LIVING WORLD OF NATURE

The Life of Sea Islands

N. J. BERRILL

and

MICHAEL BERRILL

Published in cooperation with
The World Book Encyclopedia
McGraw-Hill Book Company
NEW YORK   TORONTO   LONDON

N. J. BERRILL *was born in England and holds degrees from the Universities of Bristol and London. He has taught in England at the Universities of London and Leeds and in Canada at McGill University in Montreal, where he was for many years Chairman of the Zoology Department and, later, Strathcona Professor of Zoology. Dr. Berrill currently resides in Swarthmore, Pennsylvania, but over the years his extensive researches in marine and developmental biology have taken him to many parts of the world. He has worked at marine biological laboratories in France, England, the West Indies, Canada, and the United States. In addition to writing many research papers and several professional books, Dr. Berrill has written a number of books for the lay reader, including the prize-winning works,* Man's Emerging Mind *and* Sex and the Nature of Things. *He is also the author of* The Life of the Ocean *in this series.*

MICHAEL BERRILL, *the senior author's son, did graduate work at the University of Hawaii and recently earned his doctoral degree at Princeton University. In the course of completing his graduate research on schooling behavior of shrimp, he has studied at various marine biological laboratories in the Caribbean and along the North American coasts from Nova Scotia to Mississippi and California. More recently he has worked at marine biological laboratories in Japan and Norway. Dr. Berrill currently teaches biology at Trent University in Peterborough, Ontario.*

Library of Congress Catalog Card Number: 70-80759

234567890 NR RM 754321

ISBN 07-046011-6

Contents

THE PRIVATE LIVES OF ISLANDERS 131

APPENDIX

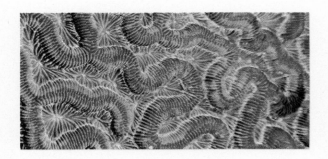

Islands of Life

Landing on a sea island, even a familiar one, is like arriving in another world. The experience is always an exciting one, even when the island lies so close to shore that the mainland is visible on the horizon. No matter how you get there, whether by sea or by air, the moment you set foot on island soil you know you have arrived at a special place. You are in a world surrounded by water.

No two islands are quite the same, however. An island may be high or low, large or small, wet or dry, cold or warm. It may lie close to the mainland or a thousand miles from shore. An island may be young or it may be old. Even when two islands belong to the same island chain or to the same *archipelago,* or group of islands, the differences between them may be considerable. And tropical islands, of course, are strikingly different from islands lying near the poles.

You can see islands of one sort or another being formed along almost any coastline. Where a river enters the sea by several mouths, islands are gradually isolated from the mainland by the force of water rushing down the river's channels.

Even more dramatic is the process by which islands form along rocky coasts. Slowly but surely the sea breaks up the rocks and cliffs, pounding them into sand and leaving islets of harder rock here and there. Where land projects out to sea, eventually the water cuts through to make one or more offshore islands. Still others, such as Martha's Vineyard south of Cape Cod, were isolated from the mainland at the end of the ice age, when the great glaciers melted and caused the sea level to rise.

Islands cut off from continental mainlands in these ways are known as *continental islands*. Others, the *oceanic islands*, rise directly from the ocean floor without ever having been attached to other land. While continental islands are launched, so to speak, with an assortment of plant and animal life already on board, the life of an oceanic island must reach it by sea or by air.

Continental islands

Continental islands may be no more than fragments of land or they may be thousands of square miles in extent. The rocky stacks off the Oregon coast and the famous pierced

Sea currents and crashing breakers gnaw relentlessly at a peninsula on one of the Galápagos Islands. Eventually the narrow connecting neck of land will disappear and an islet will stand offshore from the larger island.

rock at Percé, off Quebec's Gaspé Peninsula, are examples of very small continental islands. Undoubtedly they were much larger when they were first cut off from the mainland, but now they are in the process of final destruction by the elements. Islets such as these may be so small that little vegetation can survive except grasses, small shrubs, and small flowering plants. Animal life usually is limited to birds and insects that visit the islets, together with an assortment of worms, grubs, and spiders living in the soil and on the vegetation.

Somewhat larger but otherwise similar islands may still have space enough to support trees. In addition, very small mammals such as shrews and field mice, residents of the land since before the time it became an island, may flourish, feeding on grubs and grains among the grassy roots. Larger creatures such as foxes, on the other hand, are unlikely to survive on an island territory, or even to have stayed behind when the island was forming. This is because the relatively small area of the island and the somewhat greater exposure to the elements together make living conditions harsher than on the nearby mainland.

Compared with the adjacent mainland, then, the smaller continental islands have a generally restricted assortment of

The tuatara, found only on a few islands off the coast of New Zealand, is truly a living fossil; its nearest relatives became extinct about 150 million years ago. This slow-moving lizardlike creature feeds on insects and other small animals.

plant and animal life. The larger *predators*, animals that live by capturing other animals for food, simply cannot find enough to eat on a small island. But as a rule, the rigorous living conditions afford one great advantage to creatures that do manage to survive. Because of the usual absence of predatory mammals, the island may become a sanctuary, particularly as a breeding place for sea birds. We shall take a look at some of the more famous bird islands in the third part of this book.

Occasionally some creature may survive in an island sanctuary after all its fellows have become extinct elsewhere. The tuatara, or sphenodon, of New Zealand is a well-known example of such a *relict* species: This very primitive lizard-like animal, notable for having a third eye on the top of its head, belongs to a family that used to be common throughout the world but became extinct in most places about 150 million years ago. The tuatara lived on in the large isolated islands of New Zealand, where, until very recently, it had no enemies. Now, as a result of man's introduction of cats, dogs, rats, and pigs, which prey on it, the tuatara has disappeared even from most of New Zealand's islands. But a few survive on several minute offshore islets where there are no predators and where visitors are seldom permitted.

Life on a continental island

A good example of a continental island with exceptionally rich flora and fauna is Trinidad, an island nearly two thousand square miles in extent, lying just off the northeastern coast of South America. The island, which was first discovered by Columbus in 1498, on his third voyage across the Atlantic, stands directly opposite the several mouths of the Orinoco, one of the greatest rivers in the world. The river, in fact, has made the island, by cutting it off from the mainland. If Trinidad were not crossed by a range of high limestone mountains, it probably would have been washed away long ago by the action of the Orinoco's waters. As it is, the river has eroded a deep subsurface channel on either side of the island.

Not only do many of the original mainland plants and animals survive on Trinidad, but they are constantly being replenished by new arrivals. During the rainy season, from May to November, the floodwaters from the mouths of the Orinoco are so strong that they shoulder aside the oceanic equatorial current flowing westward from Africa and deposit all sorts of debris along the southern shores of Trinidad. For as the river rises and floods its banks, it flushes out fallen trees, matted islands of brush, and rafts of water hyacinth. These are carried across the narrow gulf separating the island from the mainland, and many come to rest along the island's shores.

Consequently, Trinidad is populated with many of the plants and smaller animals that live along the shores of the Orinoco River. Lizards, snakes, crab-eating raccoons (known locally as mangrove dogs), and small monkeys occasionally are seen arriving on shore on masses of driftwood. Only the largest creatures of the mainland forest and jungle—creatures such as the bulky tapir and the powerful jaguar—seem able to avoid being trapped and swept away. It is true, as fossils show, that these animals roamed on Trinidad when it was part of the mainland, but all have been exterminated from the island.

In the more mountainous interior regions of the island, a tropical forest similar to that on the mainland remains well established. Virgin jungle clothes most of the northern range of mountains. *Epiphytes*—nonparasitic plants that grow on other plants instead of taking root in the soil—flourish every-

In the moist tropical forests of Trinidad, the trees are hung with epiphytes, or "air plants," such as this showy bromeliad, or member of the pineapple family.

ISLAND GIANT:
THE KOMODO DRAGON

The Komodo dragon, the world's largest lizard, lives only on a few of the Lesser Sunda Islands of Indonesia. This giant member of the monitor-lizard family may grow as much as ten feet long and weigh three hundred pounds or more. Other members of the family, in contrast, rarely exceed five feet in length, and some are only eight to ten inches long.

Less than one thousand of these unique creatures survive on their native islands. But, fortunately, the government of Indonesia has recently set aside part of Rintja Island as the world's only dragon sanctuary.

At the left, a Komodo dragon wanders along a beach on Komodo Island. Like alligators and crocodiles, these lizards walk with the body raised well off the ground. The dragon at the right was lured within camera range with an offering of meat. Although they sometimes eat dead carcasses, these powerful meat eaters are able to capture goats, monkeys, and other live prey.

The heliconia, a relative of the cultivated banana, is common in the forests of Trinidad. This attractive native of northern South America probably grew on Trinidad even before the island was separated from the mainland.

where, covering tree trunks and branches, creepers, and vines. Some are delicate star-shaped plants, while others look like overgrown cabbages as much as ten feet across. In addition, there are groves of a plant related to the banana; its long, broad leaves resemble banana leaves, but it has weird, clawlike red flowers. Another plant looks like giant rhubarb, with stems as thick and solid as the trunk of a palm tree. And lush tree ferns grow in the higher places.

Amid all this lavish vegetation, scores of brilliant hummingbirds buzz through the still, humid air, flashing gold, copper, green, and blue as they visit the flowers to feed. Snakes, lizards, and groups of piglike collared peccaries scrounge through the undergrowth for a living.

The birth of a volcanic island

In contrast to continental islands, oceanic islands are likely to be far out at sea. Most of them are small, and none has any life of its own to start with. Usually these islands are submarine volcanic mountains that have risen from the floor of the deep ocean and protrude above the surface. The thousands of small islands that dot the enormous expanse of the tropical Pacific Ocean are of this kind, as are the Atlantic's Iceland, Bermuda, Azores, Canaries, Ascension Island, St. Helena, and Tristan da Cunha Islands. Elsewhere, in shallow seas, the ocean floor itself may rise slowly above the surface, without volcanic activity. Such was the case with the formation of the Bahama Islands and the Florida Keys.

Occasionally we are fortunate enough to witness the actual birth of an oceanic island and to observe how plants and animals first become established there. One such island is Surtsey, just south of Iceland, which emerged from the ocean as a steaming erupting volcano in November of 1963.

Iceland lies in one of the most volcanic areas in the world. Great expanses of the island are covered with lava flows and

The birth of Surtsey, a volcanic island a few miles southwest of Iceland, began in November 1963, when a column of smoke and steam suddenly burst from the ocean's surface and rose four miles into the sky. Within twenty-four hours, the little island already had risen thirty-three feet above the sea.

16

pockmarked with volcanic craters. Geysers and hot springs bubbling from the earth on Iceland are further evidence of the great masses of superheated material lying very close to the earth's surface in this area. Occasionally the pressure of this heated matter becomes too great to be contained. That is what happened at Surtsey. Gases and molten material eventually found their way through a break in the earth's crust on the ocean floor and came bursting through to the surface. A column of volcanic rock and huge clouds of steam exploded from the ocean's surface. As the accumulated ash and rock in the cone around the volcano's vent rose higher and higher, the peak itself began to rise above the ocean's surface.

Eruptions continued intermittently for several months, with gases, ash, and molten lava escaping through various openings in the volcanic cone. When the eruptions finally subsided and the lava cooled, a new high island stood in the northern ocean, with big Atlantic rollers breaking on black volcanic beaches and crashing against lava cliffs. Surtsey had been born.

Life comes to Surtsey

Geologists, the scientists who study the earth and the rocks of which it is formed, took advantage of this opportunity to witness the birth of a volcanic island. Even as the volcano was erupting, they approached as close as they safely could to record their observations.

When the eruptions diminished, the geologists were quickly joined by *biologists,* scientists who specialize in the study of living things. They were eager to learn more about the ways in which living plants and animals colonize new territory. Like all oceanic islands, Surtsey was absolutely barren at its birth, and whatever plants or animals might eventually be found there would have to be carried to the island in some way by air or by sea.

Over the course of several months, Surtsey was rocked by repeated explosions. Great clouds of ash were hurled into the air, and streams of molten lava cascaded down the developing island's slopes. When volcanic activity finally subsided, Surtsey stood 670 feet high and covered an area of one square mile.

A volcanic island is formed when molten lava (shown in red) breaks through a fissure in the earth's crust and begins to accumulate on the sea floor (*top*). Still invisible from the surface, the mountain grows higher as more lava flows down its flanks (*middle*). Finally, the mountaintop breaks through the surface and the island is born (*bottom*). The island will continue to grow as long as the volcano remains active.

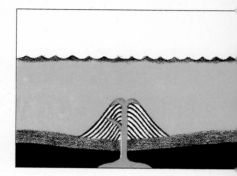

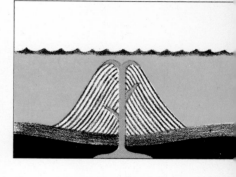

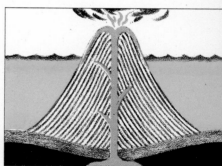

19

Birds were probably the first creatures to take advantage of this new bit of land in the trackless ocean. Even during the early eruptions, gulls came to the island during lulls and rested on the warm cinders. Now they roost regularly on Surtsey's hills and cliffs. In addition, the island harbors sea birds such as oystercatchers and kittiwakes, together with a few land birds.

Only six months after the first eruptions, scientists discovered bacteria and molds on the island. Within three or four years, they found a dozen or more species of minute single-celled algae. Before long, patches of moss were discovered at the very edge of the highest crater. And scientists already have collected twenty-six different kinds of insects on Surtsey.

Someday Surtsey may support much the same sort of vegetation as the large island of Iceland itself, for volcanic ash serves well as soil for many kinds of plants and Surtsey is close enough to receive spores and seeds carried over by

A ring of barely submerged coral reefs forms an almost perfect atoll in the Fiji Islands. The islets at the center of the lagoon are the eroded peaks of the volcanic mountain whose flanks provided the foundation on which the atoll grew.

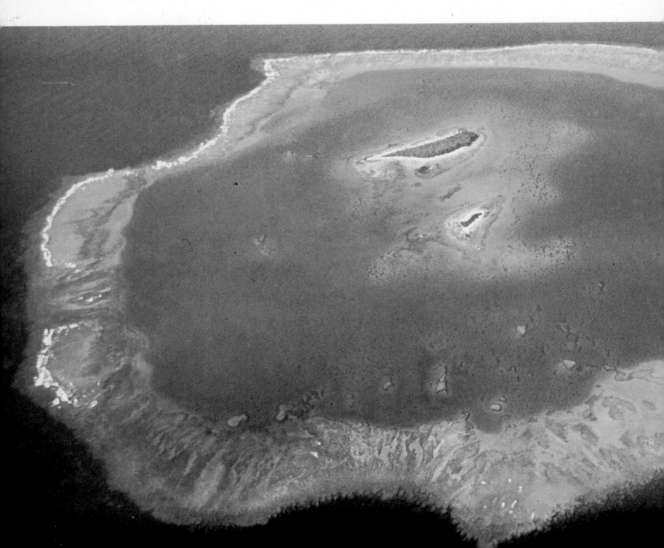

wind or by birds. In addition to the mosses and algae, sea rocket and a number of other flowering plants have been found on the island. Many of the seeds undoubtedly were brought over by the birds, either lodged among their feathers or attached to their muddy feet. In fact, Charles Darwin once found that eighty-three plants, representing five different species, grew from the seeds contained in a ball of mud he had taken from the plumage of a bird.

What finally grows on Surtsey depends not only on what manages to reach the island but also on how well the plants may be suited to the cold and windy climate of the North Atlantic Ocean.

Coral islands

Wind, rain, and the action of the sea begin to wear down oceanic islands from the very first. Sooner or later the island

At close range, coral gardens like this one on Australia's Great Barrier Reef are an unforgettable spectacle, dominated by corals of many shapes and colors. At lower center is the fluted blue-green edge of a giant clam, which grows as large as three feet across.

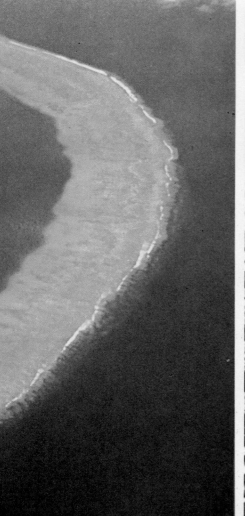

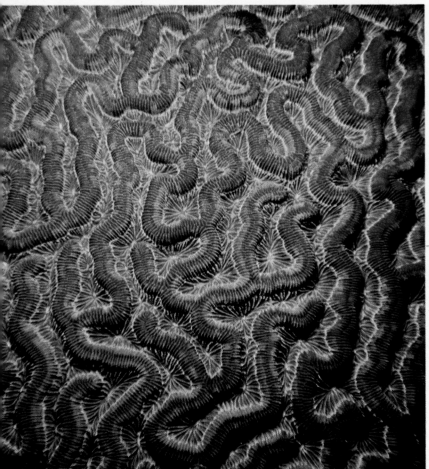

BUCK ISLAND
NATIONAL MONUMENT

At Buck Island *(opposite page)*, two miles north of St. Croix, one of the Virgin Islands, the United States Department of the Interior maintains one of the most unusual preserves in the National Park System. Off the shore of this tiny, uninhabited island, visitors equipped with snorkeling gear can observe the fascinating world of a magnificent coral reef. Arrows and numbered signs on the ocean floor guide swimmers along the sea trail at this unique nature museum.

Some of the common corals that visitors can see at Buck Island are the staghorn coral *(upper right)* and the brain coral *(lower right)*. On the next two pages are some of the brilliantly colored fish that dart in and out among the corals. At the left is a school of French grunts. At the upper right is a squirrelfish, and at the lower right is the spectacular queen angelfish.

An atoll begins its growth as a coral reef (shown in red) surrounding a volcanic island (*top*). As the earth's crust bends down under the weight of the mountain, the island begins to sink, but the barrier reef continues to grow upward (*middle*). Finally the island disappears, leaving an atoll, a ring of coral islets surrounding a shallow lagoon (*bottom*).

disappears beneath the waves. In the case of a small islet this may occur after only a few years, but larger islands may persist for a million years or more, depending on size and circumstances. In the warmer seas an oceanic island's existence may be greatly prolonged by the growth of offshore *coral reefs.*

The reefs are formed by millions of individual coral animals, or *polyps,* minute creatures that are similar in appearance to the closely related but much larger sea anemones. Each coral animal in a colony rests on a hard, skeletonlike cup of calcium carbonate, which the animal has extracted from the seawater. Depending on the species of coral, colonies assume distinctive forms that have given rise to such apt names as brain coral, staghorn coral, elkhorn coral, and so on. The formation grows as the polyps deposit additional layers of calcium over long periods of time.

Coral reefs flourish only in warm, clear, shallow seawater. The shallow shelf of sand, rocks, and other debris that forms around a tropical island's shores, as a result of erosion of the central mountain, provides ideal living conditions for a coral reef. Even when the original mountain has become completely eroded, the reefs still grow to the surface of the sea, supported by the dead reef below. Eventually a ring of living coral reef may be all that is left to represent the volcano that at one time extended high into the air. Such a ring, together with the coral rubble that erodes from the reef and piles up as islands here and there along its edge, is called an *atoll.*

Although very common in the tropical Pacific Ocean, atolls are rare in the Atlantic. In fact, the Bermuda Islands are the only good example of the remains of an Atlantic atoll. The islands themselves are nothing more than solidified sand dunes that have piled up as a crescent along the southern edge of the Bermuda atoll as a result of the prevailing winds. Except for some rocks on the northern edge, the rest of the atoll lies entirely underwater, resting on top of an old, submerged volcanic mountain.

In some areas, however, the islets around the edge of an atoll consist of sand that shifts continually under the influence of wind and waves, and the smallest islets are forever appearing and disappearing as currents change. We can see this happening and observe how plants and animals adjust to the changes if we take the island-hopping causeway to

Key West, off the southern tip of Florida, and then take a boat to the Dry Tortugas, in the Gulf of Mexico.

The life cycle of sand islands

The long line of *keys,* as these low islets and reefs are known in the Florida area, curves more and more to the west as one travels south, seeming to end at Key West itself. Yet beyond this the land continues as a ridge, now entirely covered by the sea, until it rises slightly above the surface for the last time some seventy miles farther west in the Gulf of Mexico. This final emergence forms a cluster of small sand islands, the Dry Tortugas.

On one of them rise the stark remains of a long-abandoned naval outpost, Fort Jefferson, with its great red-brick walls standing out sharply against the sky. The islands and surrounding waters are now preserved as Fort Jefferson National Monument, a unit of the National Park System.

The several islands, which partly enclose a lagoon, are composed mostly of accumulations of coral sand, swept or

The Dry Tortugas, seven islets in the Gulf of Mexico, are preserved as Fort Jefferson National Monument. The central feature of the preserve is the sprawling fort itself, but visitors also come to observe the sea birds that nest on the islands and to snorkel in the shallow surrounding waters.

Every year in mid-April, tens of thousands of sooty terns flock to the Dry Tortugas to lay their eggs and raise their young in vast, crowded colonies. By late September all the birds abandon the islands and range far and wide over the sea.

thrown up by current and wave. The islands rise only a few feet above the sea, and the smaller ones, especially, shift constantly as time goes on.

For the most part the Dry Tortugas are islands of birds, particularly sooty and noddy terns. Sea birds are fishermen, and where the fish go the birds are sure to follow. The Dry Tortugas are especially attractive to the terns because of the shallow lagoon, where they can easily catch great numbers of fish to feed their young. And so each spring the birds converge on the Dry Tortugas to breed, with hundreds of noddy terns and as many as 120,000 sooty terns gathering on the islands each year.

On one of the keys, Bush Key, the sooty terns nest almost everywhere. Each female lays her one or two mottled eggs in a shallow depression in the sand. The nests are crowded so closely that you have to watch your step to avoid crushing eggs and fledglings, and even a brooding mother moves only at the last moment, protestingly. The far less numerous noddy terns, in contrast, make nests a little more worthy of the name, either among the lower branches of mangrove bushes or in the fleshy green sesuvium scrub that covers much of the island.

The keys and terns of the Dry Tortugas are closely associated and have had a curious history. At the turn of the century Bush Key was nothing more than a barren sand bar awash with the tide. At that time, the colonies of sooty and noddy terns nested on Bird Key, then an extensive island but now in its turn just a sandy shoal. Together Bush Key and Bird Key show how such islands are born, live, die, and become reborn—in the island cycle.

At the time when the terns still nested on Bird Key, the island was covered with vegetation, which the birds find necessary for their breeding. The plants, moreover, were responsible for the island's very existence, for their tangled mats of roots bound sand and soil together and kept them from being washed away by the scouring of the currents and the blast of hurricanes.

But birds, particularly sea birds, excrete *guano,* a semisolid waste rich in phosphate fertilizer salts. And this substance,

Although greatly outnumbered by the sooty terns, several hundred noddy terns also breed on Bush Key in the Dry Tortugas. These handsome birds are named for the way they nod at each other during their courtship ritual.

ISLAND HARVEST: BIRD EGGS BY THE MILLIONS

Wherever people live near sea-bird colonies, the annual egg crop traditionally has been a precious harvest. Pictured here is the harvest of sooty-tern eggs in the Seychelles Islands, northeast of Madagascar in the Indian Ocean. On Novaya Zemlya, in the Arctic Ocean, Soviet fishermen still take 300,000 eggs a year from the nesting colonies of thick-billed murres. Elsewhere, sea birds such as gulls, shearwaters, guillemots, and gannets annually contribute millions of eggs to feed a protein-hungry world.

On the fringes of a vast colony of sooty terns, workers transfer one day's harvest of eggs to boxes and crates on tiny Bird Island, northernmost of the Seychelles Islands.

When outsiders such as fishermen or commercial egg collectors plunder uninhabited islands, the devastation is sometimes total. The Farallon Egg Company, for example, started taking murre eggs from California's Farallon Islands in 1854, when the annual crop was 500,000 eggs; within forty years, the harvest had dwindled to almost nothing. Where collecting is done by local natives, on the other hand, plenty of eggs are usually left to assure continuing success of the breeding colony.

The annual egg harvest on Bird Island is ended in mid-July so that the terns will have time to raise their young and maintain the colony. Here crates of eggs begin their precarious trip to market.

Unlike most plants, mangroves produce fruits that germinate while still attached to the parent plant. A single mangrove often bears fruits with long, slender seedlings in various stages of development. The seedlings usually are six to eight inches long when they drop from the tree.

which so enriches soil, will chemically burn any living plant it touches. Consequently the thousands of terns perching and nesting among the mangroves and scrub scorch and kill the leaves and branches. Slowly but surely the green cover dies from the island. Dead bushes remain for a while, but not for long. The roots rot, the tide and currents work farther into the sand, and eventually the sand and dead scrub wash away. Nothing remains except a shallow bar of sand resting on old reefs and covered by the tide.

This is exactly what happened to Bird Key earlier in this century. Even while Bird Key was dying, however, nearby Bush Key was enlarging and plants were gaining a foothold on the islet. As Bird Key began to disappear beneath the waves, the tern colonies adopted slowly enlarging Bush Key for their breeding colony, and there they continue to flourish even now.

In the meantime, abandoned Bird Key also has made a fresh start. A sand bar has risen above high water, and some vegetation once again has found a foothold. By the time the vegetation on Bush Key dies, Bird Key will be supporting tern colonies well enough to carry on the cycle. And so it may go on, from island to island, century after century.

Mangrove, maker of islands

Islands like the Dry Tortugas come from the sea itself. First coral sand is thrown up a little above the reef. Then rain falling on the exposed sand washes out some of the salts and so changes the mixture of sand and sea salt. This tends to harden into a kind of cement or sandstone to a depth of one or two inches, partially sealing off the edges of the island against the action of the waves.

Yet it takes more than reef, sand, and rain to make an island. Plants must become established, for any island that is not actually rock needs to be bound over by a green cover if it is to withstand the erosive action of winds, tides, and currents. To begin with, such plants must be able to reach the sand bars and reefs. They must be able to anchor themselves and live with their roots in salt water. And they must then create conditions that help build up the land and make it congenial to other plants.

The red mangrove is able to do all of this. Neither wind

nor birds can carry the seeds, for they develop on the branches of the parent tree and grow into long, heavy seedlings before dropping off. When this happens, they are usually six to eight inches long, of somewhat the size and shape of a cigar. They may drop straight down into the sand or mud at the base of the parent mangrove, or be carried a few feet away before lodging. As the seedlings grow and branch, they eventually transform a solitary mangrove tree into a mangrove forest.

Or the seedlings may drop into the swirling water of high tide and be swept far out to sea. Each year, thousands of seedlings are carried out to sea from the southwestern coast of Florida, and experiments with tagged seedlings have shown that many of them become stranded far away on the keys of the Dry Tortugas and elsewhere. Mangrove seedlings can even cross the Atlantic Ocean itself, from the bulge of Africa to tropical America. They drift for weeks in the equatorial current, more at home in salt water than in fresh.

The red mangrove has everything a maritime colonist

The red mangrove bears flowers and fruits simultaneously. The fruit (*right*) sprouts while still on the tree, and the seedling finally drops into the water, where it floats horizontally at first. Eventually one end will grow heavier so that the seedling floats vertically, with the spiked root tip pointed downward, ready to lodge in mud or sand.

When the red-mangrove seedling settles on the bottom in shallow water, it immediately takes root and sends up a single shoot (*above*). Within a year or so, each seedling has produced several leafy branches and sent out a dozen or so prop roots that provide firm anchorage (*center*). . . .

needs. Young plants anchor themselves and grow rapidly in shallow water between sheltering sand bars, sending down roots into the marine soil of sand and shell fragments. Then tiers of prop roots, or supports, spring out and down, so that each seedling seems to be clutching at the ground with many fingers. As fallen leaves and other debris accumulate among the roots, a richer soil is slowly formed. Eventually a fringe of mangrove trees, with a tangled mass of prop roots, forms around the sand bar. Bit by bit, new mangroves reach out into the shallow water, and the island grows. With the continuing accumulation of debris, the soil at the center of the islet becomes richer and deeper; other plants, whose seeds have been carried by wind or currents and dropped by birds, become established; and then the birds themselves take over, using the islet first as a base to fish from—for they need a resting place—and then as a breeding ground.

Neither storm waves nor hurricane winds can uproot the multianchored mangroves. As long as the trees live, the small islands resist the elements. Only after the bird droppings have killed the trees will the island be washed away by the sea.

Life on a mangrove island

East of the Florida Keys and separated from them by a deep submarine valley and the rushing water of the Gulf Stream flowing out from the Gulf of Mexico into the Atlantic Ocean, is a great chain of flat islands known as the Bahamas. Some, such as Andros and Great Inagua, are large, while others are as small as an islet can be. At no time have these islands been connected with the continent. In many ways they are like the Dry Tortugas, although they are far more numerous and most of them are very much larger. The Bahamas are all sand islands fully exposed to the sea, the wind, and the intense heat and light of the tropical sun. Here again, particularly in the case of the smallest islands, the ever-present mangrove plays the most important role in the consolidation of an island.

One of the islets off the coast of Great Inagua shows how thoroughly the mangrove can dominate an island. The only trees on the islet are a dozen or so coconut palms and one mangrove. The coconut palms grow along the shores of a little cove that penetrates the islet near its middle. This is

. . . By the time it is several years old, each tree is girded by hundreds of arching prop roots (*above*). As sand, mud, and debris are lodged in the maze of prop roots, the shallows eventually become dry land and an islet is formed.

35

Evening enfolds low-lying Andros, in the Bahama Islands.

the sort of place where coconuts drifting with the ocean currents are most likely to come ashore without being carried out to sea again, and where they can most readily sprout and take root. But it is the other tree, the mangrove, that gives the islet its distinctive character. This single mangrove tree extends over almost the entire islet. It has several hundred distinct, yet united, trunks and some thousands of prop roots that form a sort of raised platform below the trunks. Roots, trunks, and branches are all intertwined to form a dense tangle of wood supporting a thick green canopy of leaves. Altogether it gives shelter to a variety of animal life.

Down below, in the forest of mangrove roots, the sand is solidified into stone, the only firm part of the islet. Here yellow and purple land crabs feed on the debris accumulated in the mud. Out of the shade the tropical sun is too hot for the crabs, and they do not venture beyond the shadows. The same is true of the beautiful little anoles that live among the mangrove branches. These lizards, which can change in color within a few minutes from a rich yellow to a pinkish or greenish gray, depend on the leafy cover for protection from both the intensity of the sun and the force of the trade winds. Darting among the branches, they feed on the innumerable insects that also find shelter among the mangroves.

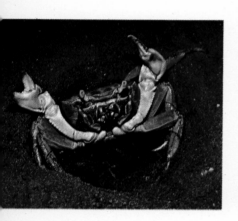

Poised at the entrance to its burrow, a purple land crab extends its fearsome-looking foreclaws in a threatening posture that apparently is intended as a warning to intruders.

Island in the wind

Such is the life on an islet. The larger Bahaman islands offer more varied opportunities for existence. Consider Great Inagua, for example, a low, flat island about sixty miles long and twenty wide, swept by the trade winds blowing from east to west throughout most of the year. Waves on the windward side constantly break up old reef coral and cast the fragments ashore, where constant pounding grinds them into coral sand. Then the wind alone takes over, piling the sand up into dunes. Under the steady drive of the wind the dunes drift slowly inland, leaving sharp coral limestone behind. Virtually the only living things able to endure the harsh conditions on the dunes are palmetto palms and land snails brought to the island on the legs of birds.

Even the birds are affected by the incessant winds. You can, in fact, tell which way the wind blows by watching the island birds: wherever they come to rest they face the wind. This is true of herons, sandpipers, doves, warblers, hawks, and many others, whether they are perching in trees or crouching on the ground and whether they rest singly or in flocks. Only where the mangrove is dense can the birds rest comfortably in other ways, without the annoyance of ruffled feathers.

The mangrove areas, as a result, are alive with water birds, which not only find shelter here from the wind but also enjoy a plentiful supply of food in the small fish that abound in the shallow water. Little green herons fish and build their nests among the mangroves. Great blue herons, stilts, and migrating sandpipers and plovers also find a haven within the mangrove world.

Where the island coast turns away from the wind, however, the sand stretches along the shore as long, level beaches lined with coconut palms leaning out toward the sea. Darting up and down the trees themselves are handsome little striped lizards, while in the glens behind the rows of trees, hordes of lively ghost crabs scuttle near their burrows.

Land crabs

Tropical sea islands, whether in the Caribbean, the Indian Ocean, or the wide expanse of the Pacific, are the homes of a variety of land crabs. Some live close to the water, among the mangroves. Ghost crabs dig their burrows in sand above the high tide line. Other kinds may live deep in the interior both on flat and on hilly islands. But however far from the water they live, land crabs are tied to the sea just as much as a frog is tied to a pond, for they must spend part of their lives in water. Each year, after they have reached maturity, the crabs go down to the sea to breed.

Most of the land crabs of the interior of Great Inagua live far back from the sea, in dry regions where big cactuses grow high above the soil. During most of the year the territory looks much like a desert. Small purple crabs, about as big as a man's fist, and big yellow crabs with huge claws are common in the interior. They ramble in the tangle of

The land hermit crab protects its relatively soft rear end by tucking it into a snail shell. When the tenant grows too big for its home, it seeks a larger shell.

39

Some people claim that ghost crabs are named for their pale, ghostly color, while others say that the name results from their habit of moving about mostly by night. Still others suggest that they are named for their ability to disappear quickly into the sand when disturbed. Whatever the origin of their name, these agile land crabs live mainly on sandy beaches, where they excavate tunnels as deep as four feet below the surface.

thorny scrub or on the barren savannas, seeking any little green vegetation on which they can feed.

In the long dry periods, the crabs live sleepily and safely within their holes, avoiding the intense sun and conserving their own body moisture as best they can. But when the rains come, as they do regularly at a certain time of year, the scene changes. Heavy tropical rain pours down on dry salt pans and dusty soil, turning all into slimy mud and filling the deep holes and crevices with warm fresh water.

This stimulus is exactly what the crabs need. All through the very dry months early in the year, each mature female crab has carried a mass of eggs beneath her body. The eggs have been slowly developing and by late spring are almost ready to hatch. But crab eggs, no matter where the parent crabs may be, must finally be taken to the sea if they are to hatch. When the rains come and the water sinks into the soil and seeps through the walls of their burrows, the adult crabs come to life. Instead of trying to keep the water out, they frantically break down the walls with their claws, allowing it to flood in all the faster. Then, when vegetation, soil, and crabs alike have been thoroughly soaked in the fresh, sweet water, the crabs emerge and begin their march to the sea.

They act as if they know which way to go, although travel in any direction on an island sooner or later takes one to the sea. No obstacles turn them aside, except momentarily, and no brackish pools left by the rain are mistaken for the sea. Only the full saltiness of the ocean itself and the rippling or crashing of waves along the beach will do. There is no stopping to feed, for the moistened eggs must be carried into the salty seawater before the ground, the air, and the eggs themselves dry out. Hour after hour, once the migration has started, the crabs pour out from the bushes close to the shore and rush into the surf. A new horde arrives every few days, until all the crabs that are ready and able to march and shed their eggs have done so.

In the sea the almost microscopic eggs hatch into strange little *larvae*, immature creatures that must undergo several changes in form before reaching adulthood. These *zoeae*, as crab larvae are called, are almost indistinguishable from those of crab species that have never left the ocean. With every march to the sea, millions of the little larvae become part of the life of the ocean. After growing and shedding

The fiddler crab typifies the developmental stages of all crabs. The newly hatched zoea larva (*top*) is only one millimeter long. After several molts, it reaches the megalops stage, more or less shrimplike in form, but with crablike legs. Several molts later the larva reaches the first crab stage, and finally it develops into a mature crab (*bottom*).

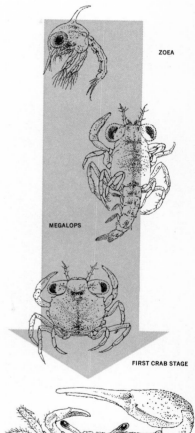

ZOEA

MEGALOPS

FIRST CRAB STAGE

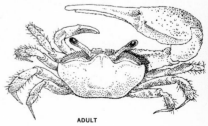

ADULT

41

their skins and gradually becoming somewhat more crablike in appearance, the relative few that survive eventually crawl out of the water and onto the beach as tiny crabs.

Even so, they are not yet ready to move away from the ocean. Moisture, if not actual seawater, is still all-important, for their gills must be kept damp. Only when the protective gill chambers are fully formed can the small creatures cease to renew the moisture by repeated visits to the sea and begin their slow journey to higher and drier regions in the interior of the island.

Of those that start inland, thousands die along the way in the heat of the sun. Some do eventually reach the shade of bushes and trees and dig their burrows among the roots. When they mature, they too will finally return to the sea, laden with eggs, to begin the cycle once again.

Coconut crabs

When it first emerges from the sea, the tiny immature coconut crab protects its vulnerable body by tucking the rear end into a snail shell.

Crabs usually are *scavengers* wherever they live, feeding on any edible refuse they can get hold of, whether plant or animal. This is also true of hermit crabs, those curious relatives of true crabs, which inhabit the empty shells of marine snails and are therefore better equipped than ordinary crabs to wander ashore from the sea, with little danger of drying up or being eaten by predators. They come ashore on many islands in the tropics, including Great Inagua.

The coconut crab, the largest, most fearsome-looking, and best known of the hermit's relatives, is found on low islands throughout the southwestern Pacific Ocean, particularly on the palm-fringed islets of the coral atolls so abundant in that area. Crabs and coconuts go together as colonists of low sandy islands of the tropical oceans. Coconuts and other palms growing along the shore of an island tend to lean out over the water. As a result, many of the nuts fall into the water and are swept out to sea and often across the ocean. The nuts are designed for ocean voyages and are ready to take root on any sandy beach where they may come to rest. Coconuts, of course, also fall abundantly on land beneath the palm trees, providing a rich supply of food for any creatures able to open them. The coconut crab is an expert at doing so.

Coconut crabs, also known as purse crabs or robber crabs,

42

By the time it is full-grown, the coconut crab—also known as the purse crab and the robber crab—may be a foot long and as much as six inches wide. With the skin on its body now hardened into a tough armor, this giant relative of the hermit crab no longer needs a snail shell to protect itself from predators.

Although it sometimes eats pandanus and other fruits, the coconut crab's preferred diet is coconut meat. When it finds a coconut, the crab begins by gouging a hole through the nut's fibrous husk . . .

may be as much as a foot long and six inches wide, with claws powerful enough to take your finger off. Unlike the true hermit crabs, adults do not wear a snail shell for protection. Instead, the whole hinder part of the body has a thick shell-like skin of its own, rather than a thin-skinned, vulnerable rear like the hermit crab's. Coconut crabs hide in holes or burrows during the day and usually emerge only at night to scavenge for food. Somehow they open coconuts with their great bluish pincer claws, although no one knows for certain how they accomplish this feat. First they strip the fiber from the nut and then they probably insert one finger of the pincer into the soft eye of the coconut to break it apart.

44

When the time comes for breeding, the giant males and somewhat smaller females mate. After mating, the female carries a large orange mass of eggs attached beneath her body. As the eggs develop they change to a pale grayish shade. Finally, when they are ready to hatch, the female crab walks down to the shore at night, climbs down over the rocks, and dips her abdomen in the sea, where the eggs hatch on contact with the water.

In the sea the story is much the same as it is for all other kinds of crabs. The larvae grow and go through several changes of skin and of shape. After drifting near the surface for about a month, they settle on the shallow sea floor and soon make their way up onto the beach. At this stage they resemble minute hermit crabs complete with snail shell. As they continue to grow, they periodically change the shell they inhabit for a larger one. They live like land hermit crabs for about two years and then discard their snail shells

... and then pries the shell apart (*left*). By the time it finishes its meal, nothing remains but the empty shell (*above*).

forever, for the skin on their hind parts is hard and tough and they are able to fend very well for themselves. Although rats and dogs may prey on them in some areas, their only real enemy is man; since they are tasty food, coconut crabs have disappeared from most islands with a human population.

The great wading birds

Great Inagua is also the home of two of the most beautiful birds in the world, the roseate spoonbill and the flamingo. These birds used to be seen in the southern regions of Florida, along the Gulf of Mexico, and throughout the West

On the Caribbean island of Bonaire, in the Netherlands West Indies, a colony of flamingos endures the vigil of incubation beneath the burning tropical sun. Each female lays a single egg on her moundlike mud nest. The eggs hatch in about thirty days.

Indies. But now, as a result of man's encroachment, relatively few of them survive. The breeding colonies on Great Inagua are among the few that remain, and even these are in danger of extinction.

Spoonbills, with their flaming pink color and their long legs and necks, are one of the glories of the living world. Seen as a wedge of great flying birds against a background of deep blue tropical sky or the green of a coral lagoon, they make an unforgettably beautiful spectacle. Their wings flap slowly and gracefully, alternating every so often with a slow glide, as the whole flock skims just above the quiet water. They are often seen flying in this manner as they pass up a large creek toward the mangrove swamps some distance in

WINGED JEWEL
OF THE MANGROVES

Among America's loveliest and rarest water
birds are the roseate spoonbills, relatives
of the herons and ibises. Probably never
very common in North America, they
were nearly wiped out by plume hunters
in the late nineteenth century. But today,
thanks to strict protection, the spoonbills
are making a comeback, with breeding
colonies found on mangrove islands along
the Texas and Florida coasts, as well as
in Cuba and South America.

The spoonbill's favorite feeding areas are
quiet, shallow, brackish pools among the
mangroves. It feeds by sweeping its broad
spatulate bill in wide arcs across the
water and snatching up the small fish,
crustaceans, mollusks, and insects that
abound in these secluded pools.

Three or four days after hatching, young flamingos leave their nests to join groups, or crèches, of birds of their own age. The adults sometimes find and feed their young in the crèche, but often the young return to their own nests to be fed.

the interior of the island. There in the shallows they search for food by wading about and continually sweeping their spoon-shaped bills from side to side in wide arcs to scoop up snails, clams, and small fish.

Great Inagua's flamingo colony is centered on a large, shallow salt-water lake far in the interior of the island. At the lake, rarely more than two or three feet deep but stretching as far as the eye can see, all kinds of water birds fish for food of one sort or another in the warm water or on the muddy bottom. Pelicans dive for fish. Terns and laughing gulls dip down to the surface to get what they can. Egrets and herons stalk about in shallower places, and ducks paddle close to shore. These are all familiar birds, to be found in many of the sheltered inlets along the southern Atlantic coast where fishing is good.

But this island lake's outstanding attraction is its magnificent colony of flamingos, which will survive so long as the birds and their eggs are left alone. One of the most thrilling sights on earth is a flock of flamingos in flight or standing majestically in the water. Here, a thousand of the stately birds may take to the air all at once, with a roaring sound produced by the sudden beating of their great black-edged rosy wings.

Flamingos can flourish only in certain situations, for they feed primarily on certain snails and other small animals that live only in shallow brackish or salt-water lakes. The flamingo's long legs, long neck, and long overhanging upper bill are all admirably suited for gleaning food from the muddy bottom of lakes and lagoons. Its head swings upside down in an arc toward its feet, like the stroke of a person playing croquet backwards, shoveling below the water as it goes. The head also rotates from side to side so that the bill turns through nearly a full circle along the bottom. As the bird feeds, a screen along each edge of the bill allows water and mud to escape, while the minute animals pass into the long, sinuous throat. Enormous numbers of such tiny creatures are needed to sustain even one flamingo, let alone the thousands of birds that make up a large flock.

The colonies, unfortunately, can easily be destroyed. Anything that disturbs the flamingo settlement—drainage of the lake, which would destroy the birds' food source, or the destruction of their moundlike nests by tropical downpours which soften the mud, or robbing the nests, as natives are inclined to do—can exterminate a colony in the course of time. Thus the birds thrive only far away from human settlements or where they are protected from molestation.

The flamingo feeds by straining food from shallow water. Arrows indicate movement of the water, which the bird draws into its bill by a pumping action in its throat and then ejects at the upper corners of the bill. Comblike edges on the bill and toothlike projections on the tongue strain out the bits of food.

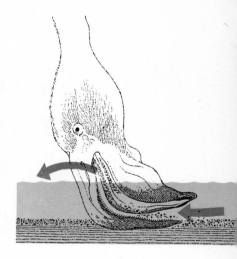

Reaching the islands

Islands, of course, generally harbor a great deal more than flamingos, snails, mangroves, and crabs. Relatively few, other than newly formed volcanic islands, are completely devoid of life. And even they are quickly colonized by a procession of plant and animal immigrants, as we have seen in the case of Surtsey.

Even so, islands rarely have as rich a variety of plant and animal life as mainland areas do. Islands are, by definition, isolated. Any extent of open water acts as a barrier to the spreading, or *dispersal,* of land plants and animals. When the water is salty, the barrier is particularly effective. Frogs and salamanders, for instance, are more or less at home in fresh water, so long as they can breathe air at the surface, but they quickly die when placed in seawater.

51

Reaching an island that is separated from the mainland by sea is therefore hazardous for many terrestrial animals and plants. The greater the distance from the mainland and the smaller the island, the less likely it is that forms of life from the mainland will be able to reach it. The difficulties are the same for both oceanic and continental islands, except that, as a rule, continental islands are closer to a continent and are correspondingly easier to reach. When they are far away, as is sometimes the case, they are as hard to get to as any oceanic island.

Dispersal by sea

How many plants and animals succeed in reaching distant islands in the ocean depends mainly on winds and currents. Transportation to an island by floating in an ocean current would seem to be the easiest means of getting there. Although it is almost impossible for animals to do this unless they can ride on a raft of some sort, a good many plants are carried along on currents. In fact, some kinds of plants are so well adapted for dispersal by ocean currents that

The widespread coconut palm, a master colonizer of tropical coasts, takes root wherever its buoyant fruits are washed ashore (*left*). Since the mature trees often lean out from the shore (*opposite*), the nuts frequently drop into the water and are carried by ocean currents to distant shores.

they are continually being introduced and reintroduced on beaches all over the world. Species of morning-glory are a good example. The seeds float, they are not harmed by salt water, and they take root wherever they are tossed ashore a little above the high tide level. The same thing, as we have seen, is true of coconuts and mangrove seedlings, both of which can drift for long distances, eventually perhaps to settle and sprout along the edges of low islands throughout the tropical world. The seeds of screw pine, or pandanus, likewise travel throughout the tropics on ocean currents. Another notable colonist of island beaches is scaevola, a small shrub that forms seaside hedges along the shores of some of the Hawaiian Islands and elsewhere in the Pacific. Its small white fruits are so buoyant that they float easily from island to island.

Hawaii's coral tree also has beanlike seeds that are well adapted for floating, and the tree undoubtedly reached the Hawaiian Islands, far out in the Pacific Ocean, by this means. But since its arrival on the islands, the coral tree has become better adapted to inland territory and now grows on the volcanic soil of the valleys and mountains rather than on the beaches.

As it happens, the seeds and fruits of a good many plants, including cotton and potato seeds, can withstand immersion in the sea for long periods. Yet few of these plants are found on island beaches, for even if their seeds managed to find their way into the sea and eventually were washed ashore, most of them would die. They simply are not adapted to endure the beach's special growing conditions of salty, sandy soil and constant exposure to the elements. As a result, the beach plants of islands around the world are few in kind, and the vegetation of one beach looks much like that of all the others.

Even more dramatic than examples of dispersal by floating seeds and fruits are instances when plants arrive full-grown on island shores. Rafts of vegetation often get carried out to sea by rivers, particularly when the rivers are in flood. When an island lies in the path of the river water, as in the case of Trinidad and the Orinoco River, all manner of plant and animal life is carried to the island and jettisoned along the shores. If no nearby island blocks the path, however, the floating rafts of debris, together with whatever may happen to be on them, are swept out to sea. These the ocean currents continue to carry along, and some of the rafted material may finally reach islands far away.

During the rainy season on the large islands of the southwestern Pacific and in the East Indies, for instance, floating rafts of this sort are frequently washed out to sea, and a large assortment of animals and plants usually ride out with them. The lush green mats of vegetation are sometimes seen with palm trees, twenty feet or more in height, still standing erect. Similarly, large trees washed out from streams in Tahiti, in the mid-Pacific, have been sighted adrift in the currents far out to sea, usually with a variety of plants and animals entangled among the branches.

The most common hitchhikers on these rafts are small animals such as insects and land snails; and even reptiles, with their protective scaly skins, are able to withstand long voyages across the ocean. Naked-skinned amphibians and

The pandanus, or screw pine, a relative of the palms, is another highly successful island colonizer. Equipped with large, buoyant, pineapplelike fruits that can withstand long immersion in salt water, this native of Madagascar is now widespread on sea islands throughout the tropics.

little warm-blooded, hairy mammals, on the other hand, are not, but those that do drift out to sea are not necessarily doomed. Although the rafts probably can travel no more than a few hundred miles before breaking up, even this is often far enough for them to reach other islands in the same general area. Given time, at least a few of the rafts are carried by wind and current in the right direction to be cast ashore.

Transportation by air

Air currents, too, may transport small organisms over enormous distances and deposit them on islands far from their original homes. Small insects, for instance, can be swept to great heights and carried far across the sea by the wind.

Obviously, the lighter the object, the more readily this can happen. But heavier objects can remain suspended if they have enough surface area exposed to the air: even a heavy man falls slowly and is carried over a considerable distance if he is wearing a parachute. The seeds of dandelions and other members of the sunflower family, besides being extremely light, are themselves shaped like small parachutes. Everyone has seen them drifting in the breeze in late spring.

If it is small enough, even a round object has a relatively large surface in proportion to its weight: thus, dust particles are able to dance in sunbeams without settling. Similarly the microscopic spores of ferns, mosses, and fungi, generally less than one-thousandth of an inch across, are so small and light that the upper currents of air can carry them almost anywhere in the world. And they are produced in enormous

Wind, water, the feathers and intestinal tracts of birds, and rafts of floating vegetation all are natural means for the dispersal of living organisms to islands from the mainland or from other islands. *Olearia megalophylla*, a relative of asters, is one of many island plants that depend on the wind to spread their seeds. Parachutelike crowns of fluff enable the seeds to soar hundreds of miles. Ballooning spiders also are carried to islands by the wind. The spiders spin long threads of silk that are blown far across the sea with the animals still attached. . . .

Olearia megalophylla

BALLOONING SPIDER

numbers. A single plant of a species of fern living in the South Pacific is calculated to set free about thirty billion spores in a season. It is no wonder that ferns have established themselves everywhere throughout the world where conditions for their growth are suitable.

In the case of insects, flies and other small kinds are not the only ones that are transported on the wind. Larger insects such as butterflies, dragonflies, and sphinx moths also have reached islands far out in the ocean, kept aloft partly by the wind and partly by their own flying action. They have even reached such remote places as the Hawaiian Islands and the coast of Antarctica.

Birds also may show up in unexpected places. Besides being good fliers, they sometimes are swept far off their intended courses by storms. As a result, bird watchers everywhere frequently note the arrival of stragglers from distant areas. On the Hawaiian Islands alone, more than thirty nonresident species of birds have been sighted over the years, all of them thousands of miles from their usual haunts.

Birds play an important role in transporting seeds, insects, and other hitchhikers over great distances. Seeds that cannot float in seawater or be carried by the wind alone may well be transported by birds, entangled among their feathers or, more likely, trapped in mud adhering to their feet and legs. Many plants, in fact, produce seeds that are either sticky or hooked, perfect for fastening themselves to a bird's feathers and feet, ready to travel as far as the bird will go. Small land snails and their eggs and various kinds of insects also are known occasionally to travel tucked among the feathers of birds. In addition, plant seeds swallowed by a bird may, following its arrival on some island, be deposited again without being harmed.

. . . Heritiera littoralis, in contrast, is a seaside plant that is dispersed by ocean currents. Its fibrous, air-filled fruits are highly buoyant and have a keeled boatlike shape that helps keep them headed into the current. Land snails depend on rafts of floating vegetation to transport them from island to island. At sea they protect themselves from salt water by drawing the body into the shell and sealing the opening with the snug-fitting operculum, a thick calcareous plate attached to the rear of the body.

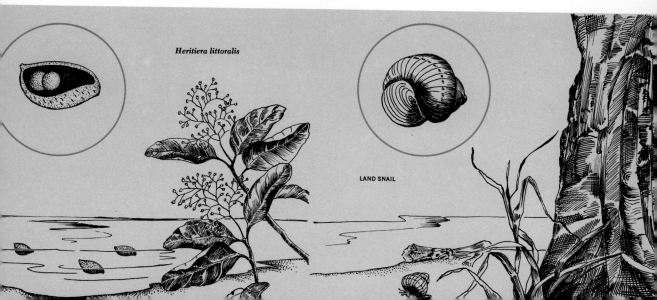

Heritiera littoralis

LAND SNAIL

Finding their own way

Sea islands can be sanctuaries for visitors as well as for permanent residents. Although relatively safe at sea, except from man himself, creatures such as the sea turtles, sea birds, and various seals must come ashore to reproduce. Thus at nesting time, when they are especially vulnerable to predatory mammals, they generally require the solitude and security of an island, or some equally isolated region of the mainland coast, if they are to produce young successfully.

By some means not yet understood, these creatures are able to return to breed on the islands of their birth, even though this may involve a trip of thousands of miles. One of the most extraordinary breeding migrations is made by the slender-billed shearwaters. The birds spend their summers feeding in the waters among Alaskan islands, where they are known as whalebirds, but for breeding purposes they congregate on small islands along the southern coast of Australia. Each May the mature birds arrive on the breeding islands over the course of three or four days, having flown to a virtual speck on the map from various regions thousands of miles away in the North Pacific. No one knows how they find their way. Yet other sea birds perform similar feats, as do seals and their relatives.

So do some sea turtles, despite their small brains and slow means of travel. They no longer are nearly so abundant as they were in the past, when they used to come ashore to lay their eggs on sandy beaches of islands and mainland coasts throughout the Caribbean. Now only small numbers of the loggerheads, leatherbacks, hawksbills, ridleys, and green turtles arrive here and there on shore to lay their eggs.

The green turtles have an especially interesting story. These great beasts, weighing perhaps five hundred pounds, feed on turtle grass, a land plant that has invaded the shallow sea in certain areas of the tropics. But even if they usually remain near shore in the beds of turtle grass, green turtles nevertheless can migrate over long distances, for

With legs modified into powerful flippers, green turtles are well equipped to spend most of their lives at sea. The females come ashore only to lay their eggs, sometimes after traveling hundreds or even thousands of miles from their feeding grounds to the secluded island beaches where they breed.

The green-turtle hatchling's existence is a series of perils. If dogs, raccoons, or other predators do not discover and dig out the eggs, a hungry gull may snatch the newly hatched turtle as it makes its way to the sea. And if it reaches the water safely, it may fall prey to sharks, barracudas, or fishermen.

feeding grounds and breeding grounds are rarely the same. The two places may be a dozen miles apart or more than a thousand.

Those feeding in the beds of turtle grass along the eastern coast of Trinidad, for example, probably make much the same journey as those that live along the northern coast of Brazil. It is a remarkable migration, for green turtles living in this area travel to one of the most isolated islands in the world—Ascension Island, in the southern tropical Atlantic Ocean—when they are ready to lay eggs.

Zoologists have marked great numbers of green-turtle hatchlings with tags as they left their nests in the sand of Ascension Island beaches. As a result, they can easily be recognized if they are later caught when they reach distant feeding areas. Many of the marked turtles have in fact turned up along Brazilian beaches, fourteen hundred miles away. Perhaps they were unavoidably carried there by the equatorial currents that move westward from Africa toward Brazil and the Caribbean. Nevertheless, fourteen hundred miles is a very long distance to travel in a vast ocean, especially when you consider how small the hatchlings are when their journey begins.

Even more astonishing is the ability of the adults to find their way back to Ascension Island when it comes time for them to nest. Certainly they are more powerful than the young turtles, and possibly they would have no difficulty swimming against the currents, if that is the way they return. But it is hard to understand how they find their way, for Ascension Island is an extremely small speck of land in a very large ocean.

The green turtles undoubtedly have some sort of compass sense, as do many birds and, apparently, sea mammals too. Even the hatchlings somehow sense the direction in which they must travel to reach the sea when they leave the nest, although the clue that attracts them appears to be some quality of light over open water.

If we are to unravel the mystery of how the breeding turtles find their way back to Ascension Island and other remote nesting areas, we must first determine exactly what

Turned on their backs, live green turtles are helpless as they are loaded on a cart, to be hauled to market on the Seychelles Islands. The females are easily captured when they come ashore to lay their eggs.

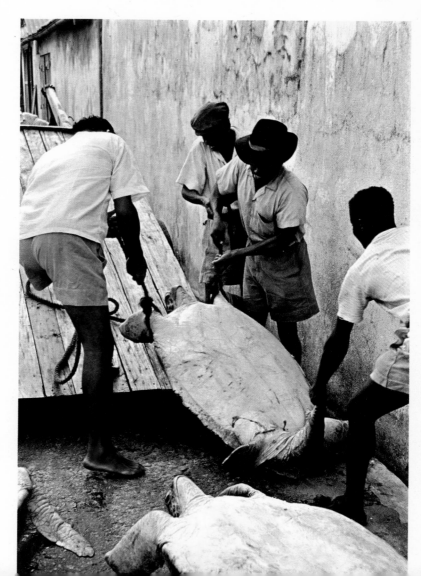

course they follow. In some instances, scientists have actually been able to plot their course by equipping both young and mature turtles with miniature radio transmitters, which reported the location of individual turtles to a space satellite each time the satellite passed within range. Even so, the most puzzling question still remains unanswered: how are the turtles able to maintain their course?

Island sanctuaries

Altogether, as we have seen, islands are places of safety. They may not harbor so rich a variety of life as mainland areas do, but they may be less crowded and less competitive than many of the plant and animal communities on the mainland. For those forms of life that do manage to reach their shores, islands often serve as sanctuaries, where particular plants and animals can succeed far better than they would anywhere else. And they may serve as breeding sanctuaries for temporary visitors who could not safely or practically breed in the same areas where they feed.

Yet if islands are places of safety, they are also, in a sense, prisons. Many of the plants and animals that have drifted to islands by one means or another have made a one-way voyage. As we shall see, strange things have happened over the course of time to the descendants of these chance wayfarers, who have found themselves trapped on an island prison.

Well beyond the reach of the crashing surf below, a group of cormorants rests between fishing forays on an isolated rocky stack off the coast of California's Santa Cruz Island. For island creatures, even the smallest bit of dry land projecting from the sea may provide a place of sanctuary.

Islands of Evolution

Strewn across the vast expanse of the Pacific Ocean are countless volcanic islands. Some form island chains, some are scattered over broad areas, and others form close groups, or archipelagos. But all of them, whether large or small, old or young, are similar in their origins. They were formed by volcanoes that rose directly from the ocean floor until they protruded above the surface of the sea.

Some of the Pacific islands are very high indeed. The island of Hawaii, at the southeastern end of the Hawaiian chain of islands, for example, rises about 13,500 feet above the sea. But if its base stood on dry land, the volcanic mountain that forms the island would rise 2000 feet above 29,000-foot-high Mount Everest, the highest peak in the world.

Others, such as Midway and Laysan, on the other hand, are flat sandy islands that barely protrude above the surface of the sea. Over the course of time, the action of wind and rain has eroded their exposed peaks nearly to sea level. Yet beneath the surface we find that they too are remnants of great volcanic mountains that were thrust up long ago from the ocean floor.

Obviously, none of these isolated volcanic islands supported any life when it was first formed. But in time all of them were colonized by an assortment of plants and animals. With the further passage of time, many of the original colonists changed in various ways, so that some of the islands now harbor plants and animals found nowhere else in the world.

Darwin's islands

For naturalists, the most intriguing of the Pacific islands are those forming the Galápagos archipelago, a group of fifteen large islands and countless islets lying more or less on the equator, about six hundred miles west of Ecuador. All the islands have been built by volcanoes rising from a large platform that stands one to two thousand feet below the surface of the ocean. One island consists of six large volcanoes, but most of the others have been built by a single volcano.

For the most part, the islands look rather desolate and forbidding, pockmarked as they are with craters, scarred by solidified lava streams, and strewn with volcanic cinders and ash. Yet they harbor an astonishing array of very unusual animals and plants, which make for fascinating scientific study. In addition, naturalists are eternally interested in the islands because of their importance to the history of science, for it was his observations of the puzzling life of the Galá-

On San Salvador in the Galápagos, a relatively recent flow of molten lava solidified into liquid patterns as it oozed across a jumble of much older volcanic rocks. Sights like this, common throughout the islands, provide convincing evidence of the archipelago's volcanic origin.

pagos that eventually led Charles Darwin, the famous nineteenth-century naturalist, to his theory of *evolution,* the process by which new forms of plant and animal life arise from forms that lived in the past.

Darwin visited the Galápagos in 1835, when he was a young man serving as a naturalist on the ship H.M.S. *Beagle.* He wrote in his journal:

> The *Beagle* arrived at the southernmost of the Galápagos islands, of which five much exceed the others in size. . . . The constitution of the whole is volcanic. I do not hesitate to affirm that there must be at least two thousand craters. The natural history is very remarkable. It seems to be a little world within itself, the greater number of its inhabitants, both vegetable and animal, being found nowhere else.

His first walk, among little craters on a glowing hot day, brought him face to face with two tortoises, each one a two-hundred-pounder, busy eating cactus. They looked at him, hissed, and slowly walked away. Large as they were, they were still in the early prime of life, for the Galápagos tortoise may weigh nearly six hundred pounds when fully grown. Two other reptiles also held his attention. Along the shores the rocks abounded with great black lizards between three and four feet in length, and on the hills another kind of giant lizard was just as common.

These three great reptiles—the giant tortoises, marine iguanas, and land iguanas—impress the visitor even to this

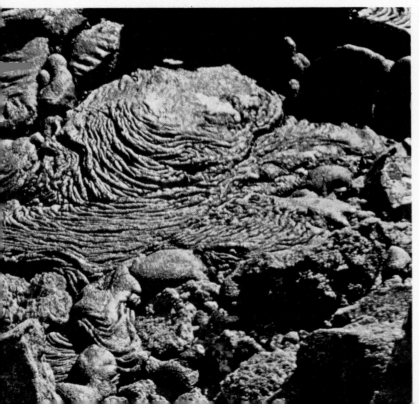

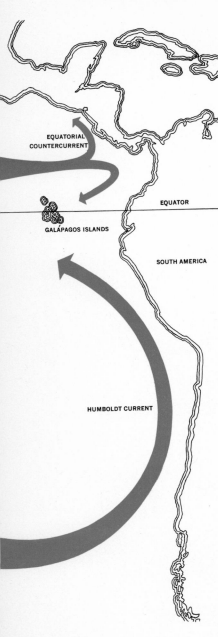

day, although they were much more numerous when Darwin landed in the isles and still more numerous when buccaneers were raiding the islands for food nearly three hundred years ago. William Dampier, the seventeenth-century pirate-naturalist, estimated that there were enough tortoises on the Galápagos to support an army of men for several months.

Even if the giant reptiles are less abundant now than they were in the past, the Galápagos are still remarkable for their intriguing assortment of native life forms. And these peculiar creatures present us with some fascinating questions. How did they reach these islands, so far from the American mainland, in the first place? And what has happened to these plants and animals since their arrival on the islands?

Drifting to the islands

All the island vegetation and animals undoubtedly came to the Galápagos either by air or by water. Both winds and ocean currents flow toward the islands from the coast of South America. The trade winds sweep constantly toward the equator from the southeast, and the cold Humboldt Current, which flows northward along the coast from Antarctica, is deflected out to sea off Peru as the South Equatorial Current.

Birds blown off course by strong winds, or perhaps just lost, could see islands such as the Galápagos from afar and would make landings if they could. Many certainly have done so. Plant seeds carried by the birds might well germinate and take root in the rich volcanic soil. At the same time, tree trunks and rafts of jungle vegetation might be swept out to sea from mainland rivers. In fact, even now such rafts are sighted from time to time, drifting in the general direction of the Galápagos. In the past this was even more likely to happen, since at times rainfall and river outflow have been much greater than now, and the ocean currents themselves sometimes have taken a more promising course.

During the millions of years that this sort of thing has been going on, once in a great while a raft of vegetation has been cast ashore on the Galápagos. And even less frequently, the raft has been carrying a female animal, perhaps a lizard or a centipede, laden with fertile or developing eggs.

When the Galápagos Islands were first discovered by man,

Ocean currents have been a major factor in colonization of the Galápagos Islands. Many forms of life, such as the Galápagos penguin, undoubtedly drifted to the islands from South America on the cool, northward-flowing Humboldt Current. Others probably were swept down from Central America on the warm Equatorial Countercurrent.

68

practically the only kinds of animals living there were reptiles, birds, and insects. The birds, of course, were able to fly to the islands. The insects either flew, were blown by the wind, or drifted in on rafts of vegetation. Reptiles, likewise, could survive the long journey adrift in the ocean, since their scaly skins enable them to withstand submersion in seawater. Amphibians, such as frogs, toads, and salamanders, on the other hand, have moist, unprotected skins and cannot tolerate any prolonged submersion in salt water. So it is not surprising that there are no amphibians on the islands.

Aside from marine species such as sea lions and fur seals, the only mammals present were one species of bat, which of course can fly, and a single species of rat. The rat's lonely presence on the islands shows how much more hazardous a long sea journey must be for a mammal than for a reptile, since mammals drown much more readily. Without any doubt, most of the mammals that drifted away from the mainland on rafts of vegetation must have died long before reaching the islands.

The Galápagos Islands, a province of Ecuador, straddle the equator about 650 miles west of South America. Here the sixteen major islands in the archipelago are identified first by their official Ecuadorian names and then by the names given to them by early English sailors. Although the English names still are used in many accounts, this text uses only the Ecuadorian names.

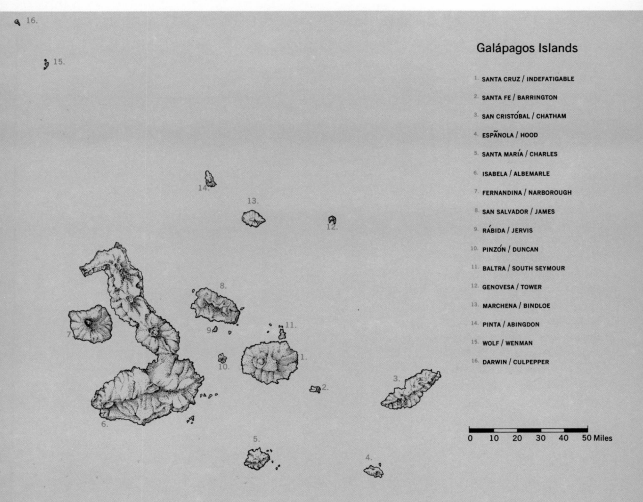

Galápagos Islands

1. SANTA CRUZ / INDEFATIGABLE
2. SANTA FE / BARRINGTON
3. SAN CRISTÓBAL / CHATHAM
4. ESPAÑOLA / HOOD
5. SANTA MARÍA / CHARLES
6. ISABELA / ALBEMARLE
7. FERNANDINA / NARBOROUGH
8. SAN SALVADOR / JAMES
9. RÁBIDA / JERVIS
10. PINZÓN / DUNCAN
11. BALTRA / SOUTH SEYMOUR
12. GENOVESA / TOWER
13. MARCHENA / BINDLOE
14. PINTA / ABINGDON
15. WOLF / WENMAN
16. DARWIN / CULPEPPER

0 10 20 30 40 50 Miles

Galápagos sea lions, near relatives of the sea lions of California, were among the few kinds of mammals inhabiting the islands when they were first discovered by man. An estimated twenty thousand now live in herds along isolated beaches on several of the islands. Here two sea lions—mother and pup—nuzzle each other as if in greeting.

The pups, born between October and December, are about two feet long and weigh twelve to fourteen pounds at birth. Adult females are about six feet long and weigh two hundred pounds, while bulls grow to seven feet in length and weigh as much as six hundred pounds.

Lowland plants, highland plants

Open groves of palo santos are typical of dry lowland slopes on many of the Galápagos Islands, but the trees also grow at higher elevations. On moist upland slopes their branches are often draped with lichens and mosses.

Plant life on the islands is quite abundant and varies with the growing conditions at different altitudes. In the lowlands, mangrove flourishes along the shores wherever it has been able to gain a foothold. A thick, bushy green shrub, *Cryptocarpus,* also stands with its roots in the tidal region. Inland, low croton bushes grow in patches of red ash among volcanic boulders. Here and there the dead-looking branches of a palo santo are silhouetted against the sky; only during the short springtime rainy season does this little tree come to life. Prickly-pear and candelabra cactuses, which grow to tree heights, also contribute to the weird aspect of the lowland landscape. Elsewhere, and peculiar to the islands, there are tree sunflowers, or scalesias, all covered with lichens of many colors.

Throughout the islands, the lowlands have this same semi-desert character. They are so hot and dry that only desert-type plants can survive. The seeds of many other plants probably land in the lowlands from time to time, and perhaps even take root and begin to grow. But the only plants that survive are those that can withstand the harsh conditions that prevail throughout the year.

Farther inland and higher on the large islands living conditions change. At higher elevations rain falls throughout the year, because the moisture-laden winds blowing across the ocean are deflected upward by the mountain slopes. When the warm winds rise up over the mountains, the air expands and grows cooler. As a result, the water vapor in the air condenses, and a light, misty rain falls frequently on much of the upland country.

With the change in climate, vegetation also changes. In-

The highlands of many of the islands are pockmarked with craters and dotted with volcanic cones. Here the landscape is carpeted with a colorful tapestry of grasses, ferns, mosses, and low shrubs.

stead of the semidesert species of the lowlands, other kinds of plants have found a footing and become luxuriant. The cactuses, so prominent at lower levels, get smaller and are covered with vines and parasitic climbing plants. White-blossomed convolvulus, a kind of morning-glory, climbs high among the bushes. The tree sunflowers here form extensive woodlands, with each tree growing thirty or forty feet high and bursting into a crown of sunflowers at the top. In many places, the ground is covered with thick carpets of ferns and mosses.

Not all high land on the Galápagos Islands is like this, however. At the top of the younger islands, where volcanic activity has been relatively recent, there is a dead, uninviting world very much like what we know the surface of the moon to be. Cinders and lava slabs, in shades ranging from black to brown, gray, and pink, may extend as far as the eye can see. In many areas, the only life is a few ferns and other small plants that are restricted to gullies and the dripping walls of dark volcanic caves. On some of the younger islands, bare, lifeless volcanic cliffs extend all the way down to the edge of the sea itself.

On the older islands, however, the highest, coldest areas

The Galápagos island of Santa Cruz clearly displays the effects on plant life of differing temperature and rainfall at several altitudes. The arid coastal zone is dominated by cactuses. In the transition zone, the cactuses are mixed with open forest. Higher up, where the air is cooler and moister, is the scalesia or tree-sunflower zone. In the cool, damp brown zone are forests of guara trees draped with brown liverworts. The miconia zone is covered with dense growths of shrubby miconias and ferns. The only plants able to survive in the cool upland zone are mosses and low-growing herbs and ferns.

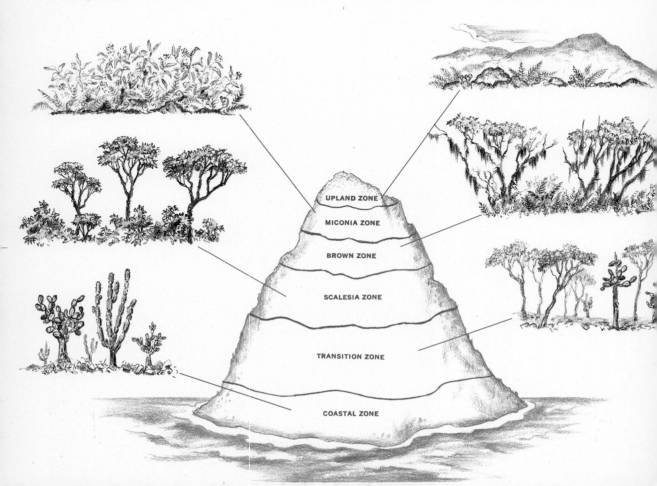

UPLAND ZONE

MICONIA ZONE

BROWN ZONE

SCALESIA ZONE

TRANSITION ZONE

COASTAL ZONE

are often covered with low vegetation and cool fog. Grass, moss, ferns, and tree ferns cover everything, and the slopes are dotted with fresh-water pools that harbor dragonflies and water beetles, just as they would if they were on the mainland instead of on islands surrounded by a vast expanse of ocean.

Island creatures

Like most islands, the Galápagos harbor quite an array of birds, including finches, mockingbirds, doves, and one species of hawk. Various sea and shore birds also live on the islands, notably frigatebirds, boobies, terns, pelicans, reef herons, cormorants, and even penguins. The penguins, most of whose relatives live on the islands of Antarctica, seem particularly unexpected on these equatorial islands. Their ancestors, no doubt, found their way to the Galápagos from the coast of Peru, where penguins are also found, having moved northward along the coast of South America on the cold Humboldt Current. The Galápagos penguins still thrive by fishing in the cool waters that surround the islands.

The islands also are visited by creatures of the sea. Marine turtles breed on the Galápagos. So do sea lions and fur seals, mammals that are well able to swim and find their way in the ocean.

As we have seen, there is also one species of bat and the grass-eating so-called rice rat. In addition, an inconspicuous kind of snake has been seen here and there, and a bizarre foot-long orange centipede also is common on the islands. But for most people who have visited the Galápagos, the most memorable inhabitants are the reptiles living among the rocks and lava flows of the volcanic landscape. It is their presence, above all, that gives the islands their appearance of belonging to another world.

In addition to the giant tortoises and two kinds of iguanas, small lava lizards and little pad-toed geckos live on many of the islands. The geckos hunt for insects at night, and the foot-long centipedes, which also hunt by night, feed in turn on the geckos. The lava lizards, on the other hand, are sun lovers and hunt for insects by day. So do the snakes, which not only catch grasshoppers and other insects but prey on the lizards as well.

Galápagos penguins, found on several islands in the archipelago, stand about twenty inches high. Their total population is estimated at between one and two thousand birds.

75

GALAPAGOS GALLERY

The oldest of the Galápagos Islands were formed about two million years ago, the youngest less than one million. When these remote volcanic islands first rose above the sea, they were totally devoid of life. But over the centuries many kinds of plants and animals drifted or strayed to the islands, mostly from Central and South America. Descendants of the original colonizers gradually changed in form and habits, so that the islands now are populated by a whole array of unique plants and animals.

The waved albatross (left) nests on Española in the Galápagos, and nowhere else in the world. The Gálapagos hawk (right), the only species of hawk found on the islands, preys on birds and other small animals.

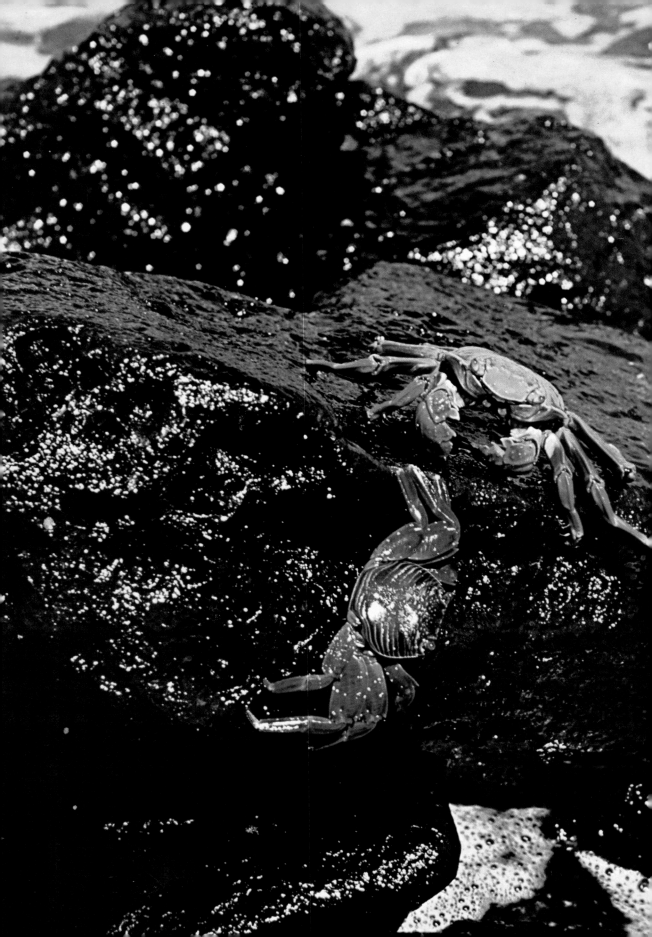

The two native crabs of the
Galápagos are the red crab (left)
and a tiny species of fiddler crab.
Hordes of the handsome red
crabs scuttle over the lava on
most of the islands' rocky
shorelines.

*The graceful fork-tailed gull (top), another Galápagos
specialty, does most of its feeding by night. The lizards
(bottom) are one of seven species of lava lizards found in
the archipelago, with each species inhabiting a different
island. The larger of the two is the male.*

Giant tortoises

The most famous of all the Galápagos reptiles are the giant tortoises. They are the largest land tortoises in the world, although the so-called elephant tortoises of the islands of Mauritius and Aldabra, both in the Indian Ocean, are almost as big. Fossil remains of large tortoises show that they once were common throughout the islands of the West Indies as well.

The Galápagos tortoises pass their days in slow motion. Like all other reptiles, they are *cold-blooded* animals, which means that their body temperature is always very much the same as that of their surroundings. Thus they do not begin to graze until about nine o'clock in the morning, when the sun is already high and their bodies have warmed up.

They feed with the least possible exertion, munching on any vegetation within reach. On low, dry islands they graze on the juicy pads of prickly-pear cactus, while in higher, damper regions where trees grow, they eat leaves, berries, and hanging vegetation. They feed simply by moving the head and neck slowly through a semicircle, biting away as they swing from side to side. Then they push forward a little on one side to clear another semicircle, after which they repeat the process on the other side. And so they continue through the hot day for about eight hours, until they are ready to settle down again for a long night's rest.

Unless they are disturbed by man or by animals that man has introduced to the islands, such is their way of life. They have no natural enemies, show no fear of man, and have as companions certain kinds of island finches that spend their time picking seeds and ticks off their skins.

Tortoises are by nature desert animals, better able than most creatures to get along under conditions of heat and scarcity of water. The great *carapace*, or shell, covering their backs, besides serving as protection against predators, helps conserve water in the body. But as a consequence of carry-

How giant tortoises reached the Galápagos or even spread from island to island remains a mystery. They swim poorly, and die from prolonged contact with salt water. Yet the Galápagos were never connected to the mainland or joined in one ancestral island.

ing so much protective armor, the tortoises move slowly and clumsily, for their legs must be stumpy in order to support the great weight of the carapace.

Naturally, they make the most of any fresh water they encounter. Whenever possible, they feed on cactus pads, in spite of the spines, since the fleshy cactus tissue contains an extraordinary amount of water. In addition, they frequently plod into pools or swampy regions and stay partly submerged in the water. Besides providing coolness and moisture, the water or partly liquid mud supports the heavy body and makes it possible for the tortoise to breathe much more easily and rapidly for a while.

On the larger islands, where there are springs in the uplands, the thirsty, mud-loving tortoises used to make well-beaten paths toward the springs from every direction, even from all the way down on the seacoast. Early explorers, in fact, first discovered the watering places by following the tortoise paths to higher land. Nowadays, however, the tortoises are not numerous enough to make such obvious trails to the springs.

Although the cool, damp upland areas offer more food, water, and bodily comfort for the tortoises, only the big males spend most of their time in the higher regions. The smaller, lighter females make regular nesting migrations to the desert lowlands, since the eggs must be laid in drier places. There in the lowlands, amid thorny scrub and cindery lava rocks, the tortoises dig their nests in hollows where red-brown soil accumulates. This they do in much the same manner as do the sea turtles that come ashore to dig their nests and lay their eggs in the sand just above the level of the tide.

In the case of the tortoise, lack of water is still a problem, for the soil where she must make her nest is hard and dry. But the tortoise comes prepared. Before leaving the damp highlands, she stores water in her bladder and body tissues. Then she makes her way to a suitable nesting site near the coast, usually an area where other tortoises have been making nests throughout the years. Once she finds such a place, exposed to full sunlight during the day so that the soil constantly remains warm enough for the eggs to develop, she begins to make a nest cavity. She starts by urinating on the dry soil to turn it into soft mud. Then she places a stumpy hind foot in the middle of the soft lava and rotates

Apparently oblivious of the spines, a giant tortoise munches on its favorite food, the fleshy pad of a prickly-pear cactus.

82

it this way and that, at the same time squeezing downward. By repeating the process, she eventually makes a hole about ten inches deep and eight inches across, into which she lays a dozen or so eggs, each one about the size of a golf ball. Finally she presses mud into the hole with the flat underside of her shell.

The soil in the nest soon dries out and sets hard. Apparently it is only after a rare rainfall that the ground again becomes soft enough for the young hatchling tortoises to dig their way out. Many of the hatchlings die in their nests because the ground remains too hard for them to escape, but enough evidently succeed in doing so to assure continuation of the species.

A giant tortoise wanders across the lush highlands of Santa Cruz. In moist areas, where there are no cactuses, the tortoises browse on leaves, berries, and other plant foods.

Giants in danger

Before the Galápagos were discovered, over four hundred years ago, the giant tortoises lived their lives unmolested. A great many were present on most of the islands, their numbers limited only by the food supply and the availability of suitable nesting places. Sufficient eggs were laid and enough newly hatched tortoises dug their way to the surface of the dry soil to keep the tortoise population at its peak.

With the coming of the buccaneers and, later, the whalers and settlers, all of this changed, and the tortoises are now in danger of extinction. Man himself is one of their greatest enemies, and the animals he has introduced to the islands are the others. Both the buccaneers and the whalers used to call at the islands to rest and stock up with food and water. Throughout the eighteenth and nineteenth centuries, ship after ship took aboard as many tortoises as they had room for, often several hundred at a time. One ship alone, in 1912, loaded about fourteen tons of tortoises in four days, almost all of them females. In all, hundreds of thousands of the great reptiles were slaughtered for food by the crews of sailing vessels.

When settlers arrived on the islands, they killed the largest tortoises they could find, particularly the huge males, just to boil them down for oil. Just as damaging were the settlers' domestic animals, many of which ran wild and played havoc in their own way. In many areas, wild goats stripped the vegetation on which the tortoises depended. They not only competed for the same food, but also were much more successful at obtaining it.

Practically since the time of their discovery, the islands have also been plagued by rats that came ashore from visiting ships. With the arrival of settlers, the rats were joined by wild dogs, cats, and pigs, all of which destroy the nests and young tortoises. Wild dogs, especially, are a constant menace, from the time a tortoise egg is laid until the young tortoise is a foot long. In the face of such heavy predation, it is doubtful whether one young tortoise out of ten thousand now survives.

The net result of all this has been an almost incredible reduction in the tortoises' abundance. At one time the great reptiles were found on eleven of the main islands. Now they are fairly numerous on only two islands, Isabela and Santa Cruz. The largest population, on Santa Cruz, is estimated at between fifteen hundred and two thousand individuals. Elsewhere they are extremely rare or have been completely exterminated.

Giant lizards

The other large reptiles of the Galápagos Islands are in their own way as striking as the giant tortoises. Both are iguanas. One is a land iguana, quite similar to those inhabiting the tropical mainland of Central and South America. The other, a related species, is a good deal more unusual, however, for it has become marine, at least so far as its food supply is concerned. It is, in fact, the only marine iguana found anywhere in the world.

Like the giant tortoises, the land iguanas are suffering severely from occupation of the islands by man and the creatures that accompany him. Darwin reported that on San Salvador they covered the ground so thickly that he could find no place to pitch his tent. Now they are no longer to be seen on the island. The story is similar almost everywhere in the Galápagos. On Baltra, in the late 1920s, William Beebe saw land iguanas under nearly every cactus bush. But after World War II, during which the island was occupied as a military base, no iguanas were left. Today they survive in numbers chiefly on some of the smaller islands.

A full-grown land iguana is a splendid animal. The largest specimens, which may be as much as four or five feet long, look impressively dragonlike, with their well-developed combs of stout, horny spines along the napes of their necks.

Each island appears to have its own variety of land iguana. On most of the islands they are blue-black and gray, with yellow on the underside. But on some of the islands they are more colorful. Those on Santa Fe have light yellow bodies, while on Fernandina the yellow bodies are further accentuated by red spots on the legs.

All the land iguanas are vegetarians. Their powerful jaws can bite off almost any foliage they encounter, including the spiny joints of the prickly-pear cactus. And wherever they live, each male has his own territory in which he digs a burrow in the light volcanic pumice rock, with his mate's burrow usually nearby.

The Galápagos land iguanas are much less common today than the marine iguanas. Formerly abundant throughout the archipelago, they are now confined to the central islands.

A lizard that swims

The marine iguanas are even more spectacular. Nearly as large as the land iguanas, their three-foot-long bodies are

85

Profiles of the five-foot-long land iguana (*left*) and the three-foot-long marine iguana (*right*) reflect conspicuous differences in their feeding habits. The land iguana uses its slightly pointed snout to pluck leaves, shoots, berries, and bark from land plants. Like the giant tortoise, it even eats the pads of prickly-pear cactuses. The

marine iguana, in contrast, has a broad, blunt snout that
enables it to crop close-growing seaweed from rocks
along the shore and even underwater. This excellent
swimmer is sometimes seen calmly feeding on the bottom
in well over ten feet of water.

usually sooty black from head to tail, although on some islands they are blotched with red and other colors.

These big lizards are so closely tied to the rocky coasts that they seldom venture more than about ten yards inland. But what is most astonishing is their ability to swim. In the sea they cruise about with perfect ease by means of sinuous movements of the body and somewhat flattened tail, with their limbs held back against their sides. They feed on the green seaweed that grows on rocks along the shore and beneath the water just offshore.

For the most part the lizards graze on the weeds growing on rocks that are exposed at low tide, but they can just as readily dive into the water and feed while completely submerged. They can, in fact, remain underwater for over an hour. Some have been seen calmly resting on the bottom in well over ten feet of water, where they make a strange sight indeed, sitting on the rocks among hovering schools of fish.

On land they live among the jumbled lava rocks along the shore, where rocky crevices afford shelter and as much safety as they need. During the day they either bask in the hot sun or feed on seaweed along the shore. At night they tend to crawl into crevices among the rocks of the intertidal zone itself, the area alternately covered by water and exposed to air with the rise and fall of the tide. If the tide happens to be rising at the time, they may spend most of the night actually submerged under the water in their rocky crevices.

Before man and his imported creatures arrived on the islands, the marine iguanas had no enemies on land. Then, as now, their greatest threat came from the sea, for sharks infest the waters around the islands. The remains of iguanas have often been found in the bellies of sharks. The lizards are in greatest danger of attack at high tide, when the sharks swim close inshore, and they appear most reluctant to enter the water when the tide is rising.

Each male iguana occupies an outcropping of rock, which he shares only with several somewhat smaller females. If another male comes too close, each tries to scare the other away by strutting up and down, raising the comb on his head and neck, and showing the red inside his mouth. Actual fights rarely occur, however, and as a rule one or the other becomes intimidated and slowly walks away.

Apparently undaunted by the lizard's size, a Galápagos mockingbird peers curiously at a marine iguana on Española, where these ceatures are characteristically blotched with red. Long, strong claws enable the iguana to cling to slippery rocks even when surf breaks over them.

During the breeding season the females may fight on the egg-laying grounds. Such competition is bound to occur when territory suitable for nesting is so scarce. The actual nest is a hole about one foot deep, dug by the female in the black sandy areas of the beach. Once she has deposited her two eggs—the only ones she will lay during a season—the iguana carefully covers the hole and abandons the nest, depending on the warmth of the tropical sun to incubate her eggs.

Island opportunities

The marine and land iguanas of the Galápagos Islands obviously are closely related. At some time in the distant past they must have had an ancestor in common. But it is difficult to know whether they acquired their different habits and appearances since their arrival on the islands, or whether two kinds of iguanas already somewhat different from each other reached the islands independently.

In any case, iguanalike reptiles most certainly did survive the long sea journey from the American mainland, probably by clinging to jungle vegetation carried westward by the equatorial currents. When they arrived, there must already have been sufficient vegetation on the land to support them, although probably none too much. In the face of even a slight shortage of food, the rich supply of seaweed on the intertidal rocks would have been a tempting alternative for vegetarian lizards large enough and strong enough to live and feed among the rocks alongshore. Evidently some of the lizards eventually changed their habits and took advantage of this unusual food source.

The iguanas are not the only creatures of the Galápagos to have undergone drastic changes since their arrival on the islands. Until recently, the life of the Galápagos has existed in a world apart, isolated in the midst of a great ocean for an exceedingly long time. Everything that has lived there since before the coming of man has had time enough to change in various ways, to take advantage of special living conditions on the islands. There is the Galápagos duck, for instance, which is peculiar to the islands though related to a kind found in the Bahamas. Galápagos ducks are small, perhaps because they have had to fit into a small world of

Galápagos tortoises from different islands vary so much in appearance that it is often possible to tell at a glance what island a specimen comes from. Tortoises from Pinta Island (*upper*), for example, have high, domelike shells, while those from Isabela Island (*lower*) have relatively flat-topped shells.

their own. They inhabit the crater lake and its shores on Fernandina, as well as other lakes scattered throughout the islands. The ducks feed mainly on water beetles and dragonfly larvae.

Even the giant tortoises show some notable variations from island to island. When Charles Darwin visited the Galápagos, a resident official told him that it was possible to identify tortoises in terms of the islands on which they had been collected, because of various differences in their appearance.

Darwin's finches

Thus alerted, Darwin began to look with a more seeing eye at the life forms around him. Birds, in particular, attracted his attention. With only a day or so of his visit remaining, he began to notice remarkable variations among them.

Altogether he discovered twenty-six kinds of birds on the islands, twenty-five of them species peculiar to the Galápagos. Three were mockingbirds, with one kind living exclusively on Santa María, another on Isabela, and the third on San Salvador and San Cristóbal. This situation immediately raised a puzzling question: why should islands almost within sight of one another each support closely related but definitely distinctive forms of life?

Even more intriguing were the thirteen different species of finches inhabiting the Galápagos. All are small, drab, rather sparrowlike birds with stumpy tails and more or less similar voices, and clearly all have descended from one particular kind of finch that happened to colonize the islands long ago. The most conspicuous differences among them are the rather distinctively shaped beak and the individual feeding habits of each species.

Because they set off the train of thought that eventually led Darwin to his revolutionary theory of evolution, these birds now are known as Darwin's finches. Included in the group are three subgroups: six ground-dwelling species that feed mainly on seeds and cactuses in the dry coastal areas; six tree-dwelling species, most of which feed on insects in the relatively moist inland forests; and a warblerlike species that feeds exclusively on insects found in bushes in both regions.

The small ground finch *Geospiza fuliginosa* lives on all but three of the Galápagos Islands. Much like a sparrow in habits and appearance, it feeds on the seeds of weeds and grasses in dry areas.

91

Geospiza conirostris, the large cactus ground finch, inhabits only three small dry islands. It spends most of its time near the ground, feeding on seeds and on the soft flesh of prickly-pear cactuses.

Of the six ground finches, three species have heavy nut-crackerlike beaks suited for crushing hard seeds. But each one has a beak of a different size, adapted to eating seeds of different sizes. Thus, although they live in the same areas, they do not compete with each other for exactly the same food. A fourth species of ground finch has a much longer, more pointed beak and feeds on the fruits and seeds of the prickly-pear cactus. All four species live together on most of the islands, while the two remaining species, which have mixed diets of seeds and insects, live only on the outlying islands. One of these, inhabiting Wolf Island, an isolated outpost in the northern part of the archipelago, has developed a further specialization in its feeding habits. It has recently been seen to feed, although not exclusively, on the blood of boobies. It draws the blood by pecking on the skin at the bases of the bird's large wing feathers.

Among the six kinds of tree finches, three species are rather similar in appearance but vary in size. Each apparently is adapted to feeding on insects of particular sizes. Another is a vegetarian with a beak like a parrot's, which enables it to feed on buds and fruits. A fifth species feeds

The cactus ground finch *Geospiza scandens* feeds on seeds of various sizes, but its rather long bill is better adapted for eating its preferred foods, the nectar and fruits of prickly-pear cactuses.

almost exclusively on insects found in the coastal mangrove swamps.

The sixth of the tree finches is possibly the most notable of all Darwin's finches, for its habits are rather similar to those of a woodpecker. Like a woodpecker, it climbs tree trunks and uses its chisel-shaped bill to probe in crevices in search of insect grubs. But unlike a woodpecker, it does not have a long, spearlike tongue to extract the prey it discovers deep in holes and cracks. Instead, the Galápagos woodpecker finch has become a true tool user, a remarkable trait in any animal. In order to get at its prey, the finch holds a slender twig or, more often, a cactus spine in its beak, probing in the crack with the tip until the insect squirms to the surface, where the bird can easily grasp it in its beak.

The thirteenth of Darwin's finches is a small warblerlike bird. Like the warblers, it has a thin, pointed beak suitable for catching small insects as it flies in a flitting, warblerlike manner. Some scientists speculate that the original ancestor of all the island finches may have been very similar in appearance to the little warbler finch.

93

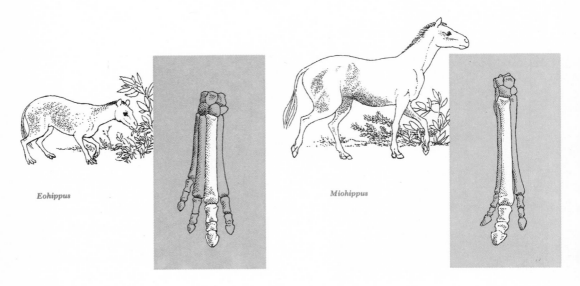

Eohippus

Miohippus

The discovery of fossil bones of ancient horselike animals helped confirm Darwin's theory of evolution. Inset drawings show changes in the bone structure of the right foreleg as the horse evolved. *Eohippus*, an eleven-inch-high ancestor of the modern horse, roamed the American plains fifty million years ago. Although it had four toes, one of them (shown in white) supported most of the animal's weight. Ten million years later it had evolved into twenty-four-inch-high *Miohippus*, which had only three toes, of which the longer middle toe was most important for support. . . .

New species from old

When Darwin visited the Galápagos, it was generally believed that all plant and animal life on earth was the result of a single act of creation. It was thought that the form and functioning of every creature, once created, was fixed and unchanging for all time. Darwin's observations on the diversity of plant and animal life on the Galápagos led him to believe that this was not so. He became convinced that every species of plant or animal is capable, over the course of time, of giving rise to new and distinctive species.

His theory of evolution, probably the most important advance in human knowledge in modern times, has influenced all scientific thinking to this day and has become the core of our present understanding of adaptability and evolution. Although our modern concept of evolution is based on a far more extensive knowledge of the biological mechanisms of heredity and variability, the essential outlines of Darwin's theory of the evolution of species through natural selection remain valid.

One of the cornerstones of the theory is the fact that no two living things are ever exactly alike. In sexual reproduction, whether plant or animal, the offspring of every pair of parents differ in various ways both from their parents and

94

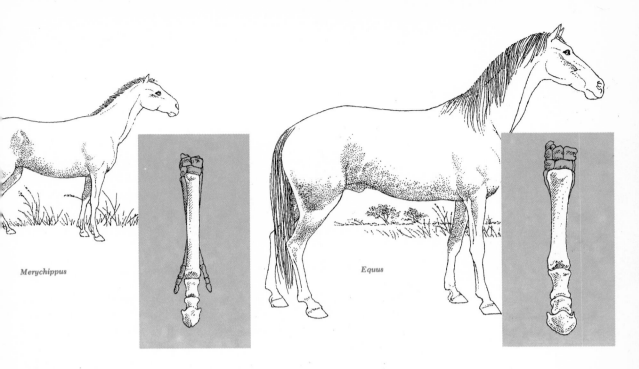

Merychippus

Equus

from each other. This is obvious in any human family; apart from identical twins, no two offspring are more than superficially alike.

Normally these variations are slight and are neither helpful nor harmful to the individuals possessing them. Over the course of time, however, every species of plant or animal living in a particular region has become adapted for a particular way of life. As a result, those offspring most like their parents are the most likely to survive, generation after generation. Nature selects them, so to speak, because they are the ones best suited to grow and reproduce in such circumstances. Unless living conditions change, those that differ substantially from their parents are less likely to be successful: fewer grow to maturity, and fewer of their own offspring are likely to survive. So, in nature's own way, they are weeded out.

But occasionally some of the offspring are born with a characteristic that actually increases their chances for survival. Suppose, for example, that a short-legged but nevertheless horselike animal lived on broad grassy plains. An individual that happened to be born with longer legs than its brothers would then have a better chance for survival, for it would be far more successful at outrunning predators. In turn, the long-legged individual would be likely to reach

. . . Within ten million years, *Miohippus* had evolved into *Merychippus*, a creature forty inches high. The stout central toe on each of its forelegs had become greatly elongated, while the two outer toes were much reduced in size. On the modern horse, *Equus*, the outer toes are reduced to mere splints, and the animal stands on the massive central toes only. Other characteristics, such as tooth structure, underwent similar modifications in form and function as the modern horse evolved.

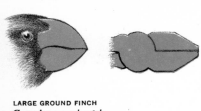

LARGE GROUND FINCH
Geospiza magnirostris

VEGETARIAN TREE FINCH
Camarhynchus crassirostris

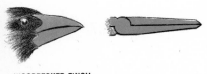

WOODPECKER FINCH
Camarhynchus pallidus

WARBLER FINCH
Certhidea olivacea

The bills of Darwin's finches are tools that reflect a variety of feeding habits. The seed-cracking bill of the large ground finch works the same way as heavy-duty lineman's pliers. Adapted for snipping buds and leaves, the bill of the vegetarian tree finch looks like parrot-headed gripping pliers. The woodpecker finch pries insects from crevices with a twig held in a bill similar to long chain-nosed pliers. The warbler finch picks insects from foliage with a bill as slender as needle-nosed pliers.

maturity and pass on the advantageous trait to its own offspring. Eventually the characteristic would spread throughout the entire population, since the long-legged, fast runners would be the animals most likely to reach maturity and reproduce. The end result would be a new species of horselike animals that differed conspicuously from those that had lived in the same area many, many generations before. And the evidence revealed by fossil remnants of their bones indicates that this, in highly simplified terms, is exactly what happened to certain ancestors of modern horses over the course of their evolution.

How the finches got that way

Islands are especially productive laboratories for the evolution of new species, for they usually offer new opportunities to plant and animal castaways. On the crowded mainland, where species have been evolving over a long period of time, almost every *niche*, or role in the functioning of the natural community, is already occupied.

Among birds, for instance, different species are likely to be specialized for various ways of life. Some species live by catching insects on the wing. Some live on ants or worms that they pick from the ground. Others glean small insects and insect eggs from the crevices of tree bark, while still others may drill beneath the bark for insect larvae. Other species may specialize in fruits and berries, and there will be seed eaters that feed on seeds of various sizes.

Thus, every available source of food is exploited by one species or another. In such a situation, an individual that forsook its ancestral food-getting habits would have a poor chance for survival. It simply could not meet the competition of other species already highly specialized for exploiting its new alternative food source.

But on an island, especially a young island that is relatively sparsely populated, there are no competitors, at least to begin with. When new kinds of plants and animals manage to reach such an island, they multiply and spread out. Descendants of the original colonizers are likely to become adapted, or to change, in ways that would have been harmful on the crowded mainland. In such a situation, offspring that differ in minor ways from their parents, instead of being systematically weeded out by natural selection, may find that their peculiar qualities are assets rather than liabilities. Various niches, such as insect-eating bird or fruit-eating bird, for example, might not be occupied by any species. If, by chance, the offspring of a seed-eating bird were born with characteristics enabling it to eat these new foods, it most likely would be very successful indeed at surviving and producing new generations of birds that shared its particular abilities. Generation after generation, the offspring would become increasingly successful at their alternative way of life and would become progressively different from their ancestors. Eventually they would form an entirely new species, so different from all other birds that they would be able to reproduce only with their own kind.

This is just the sort of thing that apparently has happened to Darwin's finches on the Galápagos. In the absence of competition from already existing species, they evolved along various lines to occupy all available niches on the islands, a process known as *adaptive radiation*. Thus some

Darwin's finches neatly demonstrate how new species evolve. All of them probably had a common seed-eating ancestor. But in the absence of competition from other birds, individuals inheriting characteristics that enabled them to exploit alternative food sources flourished and passed on these characteristics to new generations. In time, entirely new species of finches evolved, each one able to utilize different sources of food. By this process of adaptive radiation, Darwin's finches assumed the characteristics of diverse mainland families, from warblers to woodpeckers.

LARGE INSECTIVOROUS TREE FINCH
Camarhynchus psittacula

WARBLER FINCH
Certhidea olivacea

WOODPECKER FINCH
Camarhynchus pallidus

SEED-EATING ANCESTOR

VEGETARIAN TREE FINCH
Camarhynchus crassirostris

CACTUS GROUND FINCH
Geospiza scandens

LARGE GROUND FINCH
Geospiza magnirostris

of the descendants of the warblerlike finch that originally colonized the islands developed heavier beaks able to crack harder seeds. Some developed longer and more pointed beaks ideal for poking into narrow cracks for insects. And others evolved in different ways, until every opportunity for obtaining food in some special manner had been exploited. Lacking competition from other birds, the finches filled the void by gradually evolving into a variety of noncompeting new species.

Evolution in action

The lofty tree sunflower of the Galápagos is a member of the same plant family as our familiar daisies, asters, and chrysanthemums. On the Galápagos, sunflowers have evolved into a number of forms, some of them low shrubs, others tall trees.

And so it has gone with all sorts of plants and animals that managed to find their way to these remarkable islands of evolution. On the mainland, where large forest trees and large mammals already exist, it is difficult for small plants or animals to evolve into large kinds. The large species already present keep them in their place, so to speak. But on remote islands that are being freshly colonized, it is possible for comparatively small plants or animals to evolve into giant forms over the course of many, many generations. The giant tortoises and iguanas of the Galápagos are good examples. With no natural enemies and with an adequate food supply, they have developed into giants of their kind.

Obviously not every creature becomes a giant, for large size is only one of the possibilities available to a new stock of animals. When no other small creatures of the same sort are already present, there is just as great an opportunity to succeed by being small, as the islands' little lava lizards demonstrate. By the same token, the Galápagos penguins and Galápagos ducks are conspicuously small representatives of their kinds.

The same sorts of opportunities were open to the plants that managed to reach the islands. Apart from the mangrove, whose seedlings drift with warm ocean currents everywhere, the plants that reached the Galápagos appear to have been originally more like herbs than trees or shrubs. They were species whose small seeds were carried by wind or birds rather than plants that produced heavy seeds or fruit. Yet, of those that did arrive, some have evolved into giants over the course of time. On the mainland, the prickly-pear cactus grows to only moderate size, but here it attains treelike pro-

98

Not threatened by predators and having no need to migrate, or even to fly long distances to fishing grounds, the Galápagos cormorant long ago lost the power of flight. But the bird continues to thrive, for it is a superb swimmer and an expert fisherman.

portions. Similarly, a sunflower related to the common wayside plant of central North America has become a strong, tall tree on some of the Galápagos Islands.

Wingless islanders

Once a distant island has been colonized by airborne seeds, insects, or birds, the very tendency to be carried afar by the winds, which was responsible for their original successful landing, becomes a liability. Seeds blown away from the island are unlikely to settle anywhere but in the ocean, and birds inadvertently carried away on the wind are apt to be lost once they lose sight of land.

Accordingly, many island plants whose ancestors had windborne seeds now produce heavy fruits that fall and grow close to the parent plant. Generation after generation, natural selection has favored those offspring producing heavy seeds and fruits that stayed at home. Offspring that continued to disperse lightweight seeds on the wind were at a disadvantage and eventually disappeared.

To a large extent the same has been true of insects, which are usually helpless before a strong wind. Many kinds of island insects have become wingless. Loss of flight has been less of a disadvantage to them than the danger of being carried away from the island while in flight. As might be expected, the Galápagos abound with insects, such as grasshoppers, that either are wingless or have wings that are so small as to be useless for flight.

For much the same reason, many islands that lack large predatory mammals have produced flightless birds. By flying and nesting in trees, birds are able to avoid predators that might devour adults, eggs, or nestlings. Where there is no such danger, birds that cannot fly are at no particular disadvantage. The Galápagos flightless cormorant, for instance, has wings that are reduced to frail, ragged remnants. While it is somewhat clumsy on land, in the water it can swim, dive, and catch fish as well as any of its flying relatives.

Many flightless birds are very large and clumsy, for there is no reason why a bird that does not have to leave the ground should remain small and light. Thus, on islands, especially larger islands in warmer parts of the world where food is plentiful and there are no native mammals, many birds have grown large and heavy with impunity.

Three or four kinds of dodos—big, clumsy flightless birds related to pigeons—used to inhabit the islands of Mauritius, Réunion, and Rodriguez, in the Indian Ocean. They lived free from danger until the seventeenth century, when mariners introduced rats and hogs to the islands. These predators ate the dodo eggs, and the birds are now extinct.

Except for two kinds of bats, the great islands of New Zealand also were without mammals of any kind until man arrived. The flightless kiwis still survive there, with wings reduced to no more than a few bones beneath the body plumage. These birds, about as large as a chicken, escape danger by running rapidly and also have the habit of kick-

Many kinds of flightless birds have evolved in the protective environment of islands throughout the world. One of the best known is New Zealand's famous kiwi. In all, three different species of kiwis inhabit the moist forests of New Zealand, where they probe the soil for worms with their long bills.

100

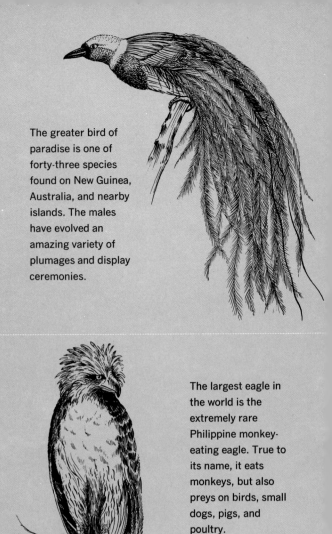

The greater bird of paradise is one of forty-three species found on New Guinea, Australia, and nearby islands. The males have evolved an amazing variety of plumages and display ceremonies.

SOME ISLAND SPECIALTIES

Because of geographic isolation, the frequent absence of predators, and the usually lessened competition from other forms of life, islands all around the world have served both as sanctuaries for the preservation of ancient life forms that have elsewhere become extinct, and as laboratories where evolution has proceeded at an accelerated rate, often with unique results.

On many islands, for example, adaptive radiation from a single ancestral form has often resulted in a host of distinct, though related, species: the vanga-shrikes of Madagascar, the honeycreepers of Hawaii, Darwin's finches in the Galápagos, the incredibly varied kangaroo relatives, or marsupials, of Australia, and so on.

Some of the end products of island evolution, moreover, are highly unusual forms, such as the strange Komodo dragon, the giant elephant birds of Madagascar, and the flightless moas of New Zealand.

Even tiny islands may give rise to unique animals. Great Gull Island, a mere seventeen-acre speck of land off the eastern tip of Long Island, New York, until recently harbored its own distinctive kind of meadow mouse. Although the Gull Island meadow mouse, like many island creatures, is now extinct, many other unique species still flourish on their island sanctuaries.

The largest eagle in the world is the extremely rare Philippine monkey-eating eagle. True to its name, it eats monkeys, but also preys on birds, small dogs, pigs, and poultry.

102

Todies are tiny, brilliantly colored relatives of kingfishers. Several species of these insect-eating woodland dwellers live only on islands in the West Indies.

In the absence of competition, the rare Tasmanian wolf, a pouched marsupial related to the kangaroo, has evolved into a six-foot-long wolflike predator.

Palmlike cycads are primitive plants that flourished about 200 million years ago. In scattered locations there are a few survivors, such as *Microcycas*, a native of Cuba.

The unique Japanese umbrella pine is a giant forest tree related to the redwoods. Now rare on its native islands, it is often planted as an ornamental in this country.

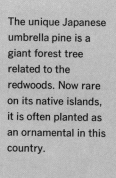

Solenodons are secretive, nocturnal, insect-eating mammals that use their long noses and large ears to locate prey. Only two species survive, one on Cuba and the other on Hispaniola.

Tarsiers are small, primitive relatives of the apes. Once found in many areas, they now survive only on the Philippines and nearby islands.

The Norfolk Island pine, one of the few cone-bearing trees found in the Southern Hemisphere, is often planted for decorative purposes. On its native Norfolk Island, near Australia, it frequently grows 120 feet tall.

ing forward violently at any offending creature. And they lay relatively enormous eggs, so that the chicks are able to run rapidly and fend for themselves as soon as they hatch. The kiwis come out at dusk to feed by probing the soil for worms and grubs with their long rapier beaks.

Another type of flightless New Zealand bird, the moas, included one of the largest birds that ever existed, standing ten feet high. Fossils show that many kinds of moas lived on the islands for several million years. Apparently the last of them were exterminated by the Maori tribesmen, who landed on New Zealand only a few centuries before white men discovered the islands.

The greatest birds of all were the elephant birds, which lived on the island of Madagascar, off the eastern coast of Africa. Like the moas, they have been extinct for only a few centuries, evidently because of both a changing climate and hunting by man. Elephant birds may not have been quite so tall as the moas, but they had heavier bones and thicker legs and probably weighed as much as a thousand pounds.

Altogether, more than a dozen kinds of elephant birds lived on Madagascar. The largest species of all apparently looked much like a goose, though it was ten feet tall. It was nearly all body and walked on short, stumpy legs, with thigh bones that were only a foot long but nearly half a foot

Like many island creatures, the boobies of the Galápagos are amazingly tame. Instead of fleeing from the unfamiliar form of a photographer, this adult and its two nearly full-grown chicks posed calmly for their portrait (*opposite*).

in width. Its chicks hatched out as big as half-grown turkeys, for its eggs were the largest ever laid. It was only when Madagascar natives came to Mauritius to buy rum from the Dutch that European scientists heard of the bird, for the natives brought with them two eggshells, each capable of holding two gallons of rum! The scientists eventually found bones and more eggshells, but the bird was gone forever.

Slaughter of the innocents

Unfortunately for island creatures, the dodos and elephant birds are not the last ones that are likely to disappear from the face of the earth. The threats to their existence come in many forms. On the Galápagos, for example, long isolation has had one rather hazardous effect. Because there have been relatively few predators, the native birds and reptiles have had little to fear; and nearly everyone who has visited the islands, sailor and naturalist alike, has been impressed by the extraordinary tameness of the island creatures. Tame or not, they probably would have been completely at the mercy of man when he finally found them. But as it was, and still is, their tameness has been their undoing. Especially during the last century or so, sealers, whalers, and

MADAGASCAR: ISLAND OF ODDITIES

One of the world's great treasure houses of natural wonders is the giant island of Madagascar, off the eastern coast of Africa. Although the island probably never was connected to the mainland, many of its life forms originated in Africa. And over the course of eons, Madagascar's original colonizers have evolved into a wealth of unique species.

Among the most spectacular were the now-extinct elephant birds, but some of the living birds are just as intriguing; several families, such as the vanga-shrikes, provide dramatic examples of adaptive radiation. The same is true of Madagascar's mammals. The catlike civets, the insect-eating tenrecs, and the lemurs also have diversified into many highly unusual species.

Other island specialties include chameleons. At the left is one of Madagascar's thirty-nine species of these bizarre reptiles. Even more numerous are the island's frogs and toads, such as the tiny tree frog at the lower right. At the upper right is the traveler's-tree, a Madagascar native that is now grown in many areas of the world.

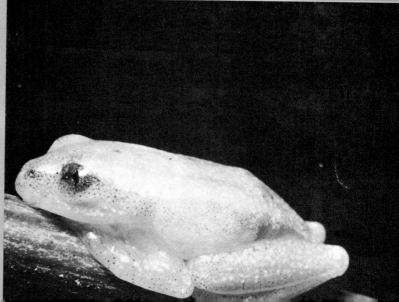

Lemurlike animals once roamed Europe and North America, but today lemurs are known only from Madagascar and nearby islands. Here this family of primitive relatives of the apes has evolved into many forms that are strikingly different in appearance. The tree-dwelling ruffed lemur (left), almost two feet long, is one of the largest of the eighteen species. Like all lemurs, it has acute senses of smell, hearing, and sight. The smallest species is the four-inch-long mouse lemur (right). It feeds during the rainy months, storing enough fat in its tail to sustain it during the long dry season, when it goes into a torpid state resembling hibernation.

Tenrecs, today found only on Madagascar, are another case
history in adaptive radiation. Some species are spiny and
tailless, others furry with long tails. Hemicentetes (above left),
an insect eater, resembles a shrew. Setifer (above right),
one of the island's commonest tenrecs, looks very much like
a hedgehog. The spurge family also is such a varied lot that
often there is no obvious resemblance among its members.
Some are trees, others are herbs, and still others creep like
vines. On Madagascar they go to extremes. The
spindle-branched young trees (right) and the flowering
"cactus" (far right) are both native Madagascar spurges.

110

settlers have been able to walk up to one animal after another and kill it with a club, while other animals merely looked on or did not even notice at all. Altogether the slaughter has been tremendous.

Less obvious but just as damaging to island creatures is the introduction of new species by man. Mainland animals, living as they do in a very competitive community, are generally wild and fearful or savage and aggressive. Otherwise they could not survive. When they are introduced into the smaller, gentler world of an oceanic island, they play havoc among the trusting native island creatures.

We have already seen how dogs and other introduced animals prey on the giant tortoises of the Galápagos. Even the native rat, a gentle grain-eating species that lives in harmony with other creatures of the islands, has suffered. It simply is no match for the seagoing black rat that has escaped from the holds of visiting ships and gone ashore on almost every island in the archipelago. The black rat, in fact, is a menace to island life everywhere, for it is an aggressive creature that feeds on the eggs and young of both birds and reptiles.

Obviously, then, the native life of islands can easily be disrupted or even destroyed. Almost overnight the unique creations of millions of years of evolution can be wiped out once and for all. The Hawaiian Islands, which, like the Galápagos, have been virtual cradles of evolution, offer especially striking examples of the ease with which such things can happen.

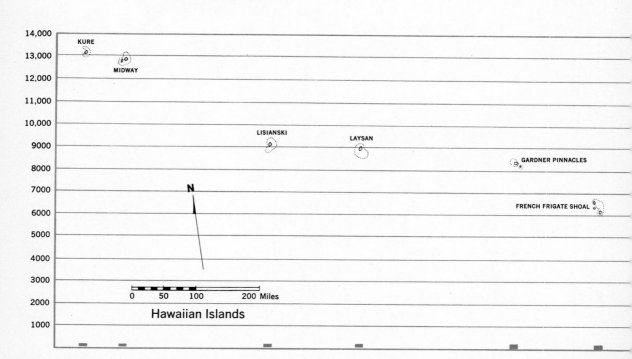

Hawaiian Islands

Distant islands

The Hawaiian Islands, far out in the Pacific Ocean, are a chain of volcanic islands extending about sixteen hundred miles in a northwest to southeast direction. The oldest peaks, at the northwestern end of the chain, form a series of small, low, sandy islands, such as Midway and Laysan, and many dangerous reefs lying just beneath the ocean's surface. These older islands were formed so long ago that wind and rain have now worn them down almost to the level of the sea. What kinds of life they may once have supported we shall never know.

The younger, more southerly islands, on the other hand, are still relatively large and high. Some, such as Kauai, Oahu, and Molokai, are now completely clad in vegetation and partially encircled by beaches of coral sand. Although quite heavily eroded, they are clearly volcanic in origin.

Still farther to the southeast are Maui and Hawaii, the youngest islands in the chain. Maui consists primarily of a large extinct volcano, with the rim of its 3000-foot-deep crater standing 10,000 feet above the sea. Offshore coral reefs have produced the island's beaches of coral sand.

Hawaii itself, at the extreme southeastern end of the chain, is both the largest and the youngest of all the islands. Its twin summits, which in winter are covered with snow, rise more than 13,000 feet above the sea. Volcanic activity is virtually an annual event on Hawaii, with the island growing a little larger year by year as black lava pours from

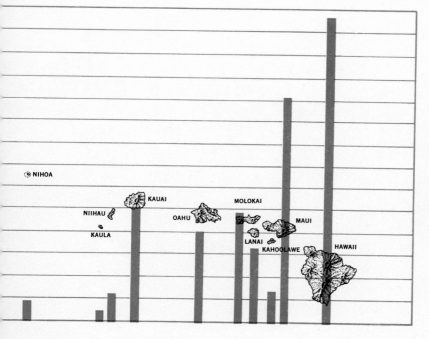

NIHOA

NIIHAU

KAULA

KAUAI

OAHU

MOLOKAI

LANAI

KAHOOLAWE

MAUI

HAWAII

The Hawaiian Islands are a sixteen-hundred-mile-long chain of volcanic islands. Here color bars indicate the maximum elevation of each island. The tallest islands, at the eastern end of the chain, are also the youngest. The much older islands at the western end of the chain have been so greatly eroded that several project only a foot or two above the sea.

vents along the mountain's flanks. On the side of the island where the volcano is still active, all the beaches are black sand, composed mostly of glassy lava particles from ground-up lava blocks.

Fortunately for visitors, large areas on each of these islands have been set aside for all time in two national parks, both outstanding showcases for the effects of volcanic activity. Haleakala National Park, on Maui, lies mostly within the enormous crater of the island's extinct volcano. Hawaii Volcanoes National Park, on Hawaii, includes two of the most active volcanoes in the world, Kilauea and Mauna Loa. At Kilauea the visitor is sometimes able to stand on the rim of the crater and watch a live volcano in action. And as a bonus, both parks are ideal places to see many of the distinctive plants and animals that live on the Hawaiian Islands.

At first glance, it seems astonishing that any life forms at all have found their way to these remote volcanic islands. In contrast to the Galápagos, which lie only about six hundred miles from South America, the Hawaiian Islands are separated from any mainland coast by thousands of miles of open ocean.

Yet reach the islands they did. Before the arrival of man, together with his plant and animal traveling companions, the islands already had been colonized by an assortment of plants, insects, and birds. Unlike the Galápagos flora and fauna, which have unmistakably arrived from the American continent, however, the plants and animals of the Hawaiian Islands appear to have come mostly from the west. Their nearest relatives, in any case, tend for the most part to be species that live in the western Pacific and southeastern Asia.

No island, of course, is too remote for some birds to reach. The golden plover, for example, each year makes the long trip in both directions between Hawaii and Alaska. But it is as difficult to determine how plants and various small animals managed to travel over the largest of all oceans as it is to decide how the tortoises actually reached the Galápagos from America.

The Hawaiian Islands are a showcase for studying island colonization and the processes of evolution. Here a pandanus, or screw pine, flourishes in a misty mountain valley on the island of Oahu. Its ancestors arrived on the islands long before the first human settlers.

THE NATIONAL PARKS OF HAWAII

In the Hawaiian Islands, two superb national parks have been preserved for the enjoyment of the American people—Haleakala National Park on Maui and Hawaii Volcanoes National Park on Hawaii. Both are ideal places for observing the effects of volcanism. Visitors at Hawaii Volcanoes National Park, in fact, occasionally are able to witness actual eruptions. Just as intriguing are the many rare plants and animals that find a place of refuge in the parks.

The most spectacular recent eruption of Kilauea, one of the large volcanoes in Hawaii Volcanoes National Park, occurred in November 1959, when tremendous fountains of red-hot lava spurted from a fissure in Kilauea Iki crater. At its peak, one of the lava fountains measured nineteen hundred feet in height.

During an eruption in Hawaii Volcanoes National Park, these trees were smothered by a shower of volcanic ash and cinders. Yet in time this scene of desolation probably will be blanketed once again with vegetation.

Hawaii's rare silversword flourishes within the huge crater of the extinct volcano at Haleakala National Park. At higher elevations, the 10,000-foot-high mountain is dusted occasionally with snow.

The rare Hawaiian goose, or nene, lives on the volcanic slopes in both of Hawaii's national parks. So that these handsome geese may be preserved from extinction, the birds are raised in captivity and later released in their ancestral mountain homes.

A major botanical attraction at Hawaii Volcanoes National
Park is the lush forest of tree ferns. On the northeastern slopes
of Kilauea, where rising air currents result in more than
three hundred inches of rain each year, these plants grow in
junglelike profusion. On the opposite side of the mountain,
in contrast, desertlike conditions prevail.

Island stepping stones

Island hopping is one way to cross a water barrier too great to be traversed in a single step. This can happen if plants or animals succeed in reaching and becoming established on an island not too far from their original home. After a time, the descendants of some of these colonists may be carried by various means to another island still farther out in the ocean. Many generations later, some of the inhabitants of the second island may in turn manage to reach yet another island. In this way islands can and do serve as stepping stones to more distant places.

At the same time it is evident that a sort of filtering process occurs. With each step forward, a few kinds of living things succeed in reaching the next island, but most are left behind. The greater the number of steps taken and the longer the steps, the fewer are the kinds of plants and animals that arrive at the final destination, the island farthest from the original source of colonizers.

Island hopping of this sort can occur only over very long periods of time. And, as might be expected, new species are likely to be evolving as the colonizers spread from island to island. Thus, as an island chain is colonized, the relatively few species that reach the most distant islands are likely to be quite different from the ancestors that made the original jump from the mainland to nearby islands.

It seems quite probable that many of the life forms of the Hawaiian Islands made their way from the southwestern Pacific by means of island stepping stones. Before man interfered with the natural life of Hawaii, the flora and fauna were descended from a relatively few species that had their original homes in New Guinea and elsewhere in the East Indies.

But how can this be explained when the nearest important islands, such as Samoa or the Fiji Islands, are at least as far from Hawaii as the American continent is? It is possible that long ago many other now-submerged islands stood

In Caribbean National Forest in Puerto Rico, the tree fern
Cyathea arborea grows at elevations up to two thousand
feet. Thanks to their minute airborne spores, various
species of tree ferns are widespread in forests on high,
moist mountain slopes throughout the tropics.

120

between Hawaii and Samoa, with their heads above the water. Charts of the western Pacific do reveal submerged islands and ridges that may well have formed such an island chain.

The surprising weeds

Among the most successful plant colonists of remote islands are the ferns and mosses. Their reproductive spores are smaller than the seeds of any flowering plants and consequently are carried far and in large numbers wherever the winds blow. And they are particularly well suited to settling and growing in the cool, moist uplands of tropical regions.

The spores of tree ferns generally succeed in establishing tree-fern forests on mountain slopes and are able to hold on in spite of later arrivals of the seeds of flowering plants. Tree ferns differ from other ferns primarily in having a main stem consisting of bundles of roots, with the fern proper growing on the top, giving the whole plant a treelike appearance. Not surprisingly, the tree-fern forests on the moist slopes of the higher islands are among Hawaii's more interesting botanical attractions.

Then, too, the islands have been colonized by the usual assortment of plants with seeds or seedlings that drift on ocean currents. There is the screw pine, a widespread island plant with corky seeds; the coconut, with its large, buoyant nuts; and the mangrove, whose seedlings are ready to take root wherever they become lodged in the shallows.

But apart from these, the seeds most likely to be carried to distant places by winds or birds are the seeds of plants commonly thought of as weeds, plants such as dandelions, thistles, fireweed, dock, and others that quickly take over wherever land has been cleared. All these rapid colonizers have seeds that are wind-carried, such as thistledown or dandelion parachutes, or have hooks or glue that sticks to the feathers or feet of birds. Thus they are more likely than

Three kinds of tree ferns grow in Hawaii, where the tallest and most abundant species is Menzies tree fern, known on the islands as the *hapu i'i*. Even taller are the eighty-foot specimens that thrive on Norfolk Island in the Pacific.

121

other kinds to colonize distant islands. Weed seeds and fern spores are usually the first and sometimes the only kinds to arrive.

One of the surprises of island life is the way in which members of the weedy composite family, which includes such plants as dandelions, thistles, and sunflowers, have evolved into spectacular shrubs and trees after colonizing virgin islands. We have already seen the tree sunflowers of the Galápagos. In Hawaii the most interesting plants of this sort are a group called tarweeds, a name that derives from their covering of sticky, resinous hairs.

Although most of Hawaii's native plants and animals appear to have originated in lands of the western Pacific, the tarweeds apparently arrived long ago from western North America. At present they are found mostly in California and in the Hawaiian Islands. The apparent leap from California to Hawaii is a good example of long-distance dispersal. It probably was accomplished by means of the tiny fruits that form at the edge of the flower head, for they are enfolded in sticky leaflike bracts that readily become attached to the feathers of birds.

Most of the mainland tarweeds are small weedy or shrubby *annuals*. In late summer, after flowering, the plants dry up, with only the seeds of their small fruits surviving to give rise to new plants the following year.

When it blossoms, the silversword is topped by an eight-foot spike of flowers. This, the most famous of Hawaii's four species of silverswords, grows only at high altitudes on the slopes of Haleakala, Mauna Loa, and Mauna Kea.

One group of closely related tarweeds has reached nearly all the low, dry islands off the California coast, from Santa Rosa to San Benito, and on each island has become a distinct species. But such an island offers little scope for more adventurous change, for living conditions are much the same throughout.

The high islands of Hawaii, on the other hand, provide a great variety of situations for plants, ranging from high, dry alpine surroundings on the mountaintops, to tropical rain forests on the wet slopes, to low and level areas that are almost desert. Temperatures range from those associated with occasional winter snow at the highest altitudes to continuous tropical warmth at sea level. And the soil itself varies from bare lava and volcanic cinder on the mountain slopes to deep, rich earth on the valley floors.

Thus, when primitive tarweeds arrived on the islands, they were met with a vast array of living conditions. And they were suddenly freed from the competition of other plants that existed on the mainland. It is astonishing to see what has become of descendants of the original tarweed colonists over the course of time.

One of the descendants, living in the rain forest on the island of Kauai, is now a true small tree with a foot-thick trunk and relatively large leaves. Another, found in the canyons and on the cliffs of Kauai, has polelike stems and

Close examination of a single blossom of the silversword reveals the plant's relationship to daisies, sunflowers, and other members of the composite family. The silvery coat of fuzz on the leaves is responsible for the silversword's name.

Resplendent flower heads adorn the ohia-lehua, a striking native of Hawaii's cool highlands. In some places it grows as a low shrub, elsewhere as a tree up to one hundred feet tall.

terminal rosettes of narrow grasslike leaves. The best known, however, is the famous silversword, a plant that looks like a fantastic silvery yucca and has an extremely handsome maroon flower. It lives on the reddish and purplish volcanic cinder cones of Haleakala, the 10,000-foot-high extinct volcano on Maui. The plant's swordlike leaves are covered with mats of fine glasslike hairs that reflect the intense sunlight at this high altitude. They are also thick and full of a jelly that retains water. The silversword, in other words, has become adapted to alpine sunshine and to the extremes of tropical heat and heavy snow.

The Hawaiian tarweeds thus demonstrate that adaptive radiation can occur with plants as well as animals. Like Darwin's finches on the Galápagos, they have proliferated into many species, each adapted in its own way to take advantage of a different set of living conditions.

The honeycreepers of Hawaii

The same thing has happened to Hawaii's most renowned native birds, the honeycreepers. Despite great differences

124

in their present appearance, they all are almost certainly descendants of a single tanagerlike warbler ancestor that colonized the islands long ago. Just as in the case of the tarweeds, they now live everywhere from sea level to high mountain regions, or at least did so until very recently. And like the Galápagos finches, the honeycreepers have become adapted for many ways of life.

One kind has a thick bill, similar to a parrot's, which it uses like pliers for cracking large seeds. Other species have delicate curved beaks that serve as sensitive tools for probing flowers for nectar and for locating small insects in the blossoms. Another kind, which lives among the koa trees in the forests, uses its formidable beak for ripping branches and twigs in search of insects and their larvae, with the long upper half of the beak serving as a probe. A number of honeycreepers also are strongly attracted to the bright red flowers of the ohia-lehua tree, one of the most striking trees of the original Hawaiian forests, and probe the delicate flowers for nectar and insects.

Altogether, the original ancestral form has evolved into many species of honeycreepers in Hawaii. But some of them are no longer to be seen on the islands. In the past century several of the honeycreepers have become extinct, and others are now extremely rare. Like many of Hawaii's native plants and animals, they are suffering the calamitous results of man's deliberate or accidental importation of exotic species and his insistence on altering the landscape to serve his own ends.

The decimation of the native trees and birds is caused in part by the cutting of forests to make room for growing more and more sugar cane and pineapples. But the main reason for their disappearance, in the long run, is the fact that the native forms are the delicate products of a long process of evolution on islands where they have had little or no competition in the past. Now vigorous tropical plants from elsewhere—such as guavas and lantanas—and tough, adaptive birds—such as sparrows and Indian mynas—are displacing the attractive native species. Many imported plants have in fact gone wild and started to rampage over the islands. Such is the case with avocados, coffee trees, and Brazilian peppers in the tropical lowlands, and with blackberries, plums, hydrangeas, and even nasturtiums in some of the highlands.

On Hawaii, as on many islands, man has introduced the mongoose in an effort to control rats. Unfortunately, this weasel relative has proved to be a relentless destroyer of native birds, their eggs, and their young.

Living museums

What we have been observing on the islands of Hawaii and in the Galápagos is a process that occurs to some extent on all islands, the great drama of evolution in action. Evolution, of course, has occurred to an even greater extent on the continents, but islands show it in a way we can more readily appreciate. On islands there are likely to be fewer species to begin with. And there are fewer predators and fewer competitive forms to keep them in check. As a result, it is easier for us to unravel the strands of evidence and figure out how various island species have evolved into their present forms.

As true showcases of evolution, islands such as the Galápagos are uniquely valuable to scientists. In these living

One of the prizes of Channel Islands National Monument, off the coast of California, is the large stand of giant coreopsis. Here this relative of the familiar daisylike garden flower grows into a small tree. Although the species probably evolved on the islands, today it is also found along the adjacent mainland coast.

museums, biologists can study the plants and animals in research that may ultimately enable them to solve a few of the riddles of life on earth. And yet, as we have seen, many of these living laboratories, with their unique floras and faunas, are being recklessly destroyed. Every new creature or plant imported from the mainland becomes a threat to the existence of native island forms.

It may already be too late to preserve Hawaii's native life for posterity to see. Except for the large tracts set aside in two national parks, most of the islands are unprotected and the forces of destruction continue to rampage unchecked.

Elsewhere there are more hopeful signs. Off the coast of southern California, two islands in a larger chain—Santa Barbara and Anacapa—are preserved as Channel Islands National Monument. The islands serve as sanctuaries for

herds of California sea lions, elephant seals, and rare Guadalupe fur seals. They also harbor some rare end products of evolution: Santa Barbara contains the world's largest single stand of giant coreopsis, a long-lived treelike sunflower that grows as high as eight feet. And the islands support literally dozens of other *endemic* plants, or forms that are found nowhere else, including varieties of oak, poppy, cherry, morning-glory, and painted cup. Some people have proposed enlarging this preserve to encompass five of the eight Channel Islands as a national park.

Another encouraging development concerns Aldabra Island, in the Indian Ocean, famous for its giant tortoises and several other unique animals. Not very long ago the British government announced plans to transform the tiny island into an air base. Biologists raised such an outcry of protest that, in the end, the tortoises won out and the Royal Air Force abandoned its plan.

The best news for biologists comes from the Galápagos, where, until recently, so much had happened to the unique island flora and fauna that it seemed almost too late to preserve them for posterity. At long last, in 1964, an international scientific effort succeeded in establishing a center for research and protection on Santa Cruz. It has been named the Charles Darwin Research Station and is manned by a resident director. From the center it will be possible to continue research with Darwin's finches, the Galápagos hawk, the flightless cormorant, the small nesting colony of flamingos, the penguins, the fur seals, the sea lions, and all the rest of the intriguing life of the Galápagos. And it will also be possible to help guard the remaining native life from further destruction.

On the Na Pali coast of Kauai in Hawaii, hundred-foot-high breakers gnaw at the bases of towering volcanic cliffs. Yet the islands undoubtedly will survive the onslaught of the sea for millions of years to come, and will continue to serve as an isolated sanctuary for life.

The Private Lives

of Islanders

Just as intriguing as the permanent residents of islands are the temporary visitors—the sea birds and marine mammals that take advantage of islands as places to rest and reproduce. Frequently these creatures congregate in huge colonies, for on islands they not only are relatively safe from predators, but also have convenient sources of food nearby.

Smaller islands that support little or no other life of their own are particularly attractive to these visitors. Off the coast of Maine, for example, the sea is dotted with almost uncountable islands and islets. And the cool waters surrounding them are rich in food of various kinds, including fish, squid, and many species of crustaceans, ranging from large crabs and lobsters to minute shrimps known as euphausids. The islands, as a result, sustain seals and a great variety of sea birds. They are safe places for breeding and are peaceful sanctuaries where the animals can rest at night or when they are tired from fishing.

Each kind of creature, moreover, tends to gather in groups and more or less take over certain islands for its own exclusive business. Kent Island, in the Bay of Fundy, for instance, supports an enormous breeding colony of herring gulls and black-backed gulls. Neighboring Hog Island is the home of seagoing eider ducks, which breed in the island's grasslands. Little swallowlike petrels, or "Mother Carey's chickens," also use certain of the northern islands as summer bases while exploiting the inexhaustible food supply in the surrounding sea.

A community of islands

One small cluster of islets off the coast of Maine provides a particularly good example of how various creatures of the sea can live in harmony. These islets, closer inshore but still within sight of the larger, beautiful Monhegan Island, are called Fisherman's Island, Outer Heron Island, the White Islands, and the Hypocrites.

Fisherman's Island is a treeless island standing out to sea like a tall ship, its prow thickly studded with nesting gulls in the breeding season and resting gulls throughout the year. Narrow pathways through low thickets of wild raspberry link the more open parts of the colony together. The gulls lay their eggs in any shallow soft depression they can find, or gather vegetation to form a simple moundlike nest.

When a herring-gull chick is ready to hatch, the first sign of life is its bill chipping a hole through the eggshell (*above*). Finally the chick breaks free, and within a few hours its soft down is dry and fluffy (*below*).

When the young are able to fly, the families disperse and the young birds travel from the island to the better feeding grounds of mainland coves and bays. In late summer the dark gray young are often seen trailing behind the stately adults, apparently learning how to find crabs or starfish amid the seaweed on the shore. Later they learn to break open mussels and sea urchins by dropping them from a height onto flat rocks. Most of the gulls are herring gulls, the scavengers of the seacoast, but some are great black-backed gulls. These big, powerful, handsome birds scavenge like the herring gulls and share their habit of robbing other birds of food, eggs, and young. Compared with other sea birds few of the gulls are good fishermen, but when small fish and shrimp are abundant, they do manage to catch some by diving at the water surface and picking out the prey with their beaks.

Like the young of most sea birds, the downy chicks of herring gulls can see and run about soon after hatching. The young of songbirds, such as robins and sparrows, in contrast, are naked, blind, and helpless when they hatch.

At the other end of Fisherman's Island, away from the gull colony, the scene is somewhat different. The island, in fact, is almost two islands connected by a narrow neck of gravel beach. The shoreward portion is largely avoided by the gulls, although terns nest there inconspicuously and little voles and shrews find protection in the thick cover of grass.

Island of herons

Outer Heron, as its name suggests, is an island of herons. Although similar to Fisherman's Island in size, shape, and location, this lovely island is entirely different in aspect, since it is covered with spruce forest rather than grass and shrubs. A visitor on Outer Heron, once he has left the bare, wave-swept pink granite shoreline, might well be anywhere in the northern woods. The trees, shrubs, flowers, insects, and small birds of the mainland all are there. Only the stillness and the cool salt air drifting through the dim woods recall the reality of being on an island.

Within the dense woods, great numbers of both great blue herons and black-crowned night herons gather in large colonies, or heronries, to build their nests. During early summer, the clamor of young birds on the nests shatters the silence and can be heard all across the island. Before long, the young herons try their wings in short, ungainly flights and soon begin to fish for their own food by wading in shallow places along the island shore. Adults, on the other hand, often fly far up salt-water creeks on the mainland to fish, returning to the offshore heronry only to rest.

Cormorant islands

A little inshore from Outer Heron are the White Islands, a pair of very small, steep islands. They owe their name in part to the bare wave-swept granite ledges on their windward sides and partly to the white guano deposits left by the sea birds. Both islands have been wooded in the past, but now only a few dead trunks surmount the one, and on the other the trees struggle hard for survival.

Cormorants, which nest on the islands, build in trees whenever they can. They construct their nests of sticks, if

On Outer Heron Island, off the coast of Maine, two species of herons live side by side, the black-crowned night heron (*upper*) and the great blue heron (*lower*).

As long as they can find the proper combination of isolation and proximity to fishing grounds, double-crested cormorants are quite flexible in their nesting requirements. On islands off the coast of Maine they often nest in tall spruces, and continue to do so even after the trees have been killed by their droppings. When the dead trees finally fall, the cormorants nest just as readily on the rocky ground.

any are available, and also use weed stalks, rockweed, kelp, and other debris. But no matter how healthy the nest trees may be to begin with, guano droppings on the foliage eventually kill them. Even so, the nesting goes on in the dead trees year after year until the trees finally fall, either from rot or from the force of winter winds. Then all the birds must nest on the ground, so far as there is room.

The young, sometimes four to a nest, are fed by both parents. They grow rapidly on semiliquid food which they take by reaching into the adult's throat with their bills. After three or four weeks, they are almost fully grown, although still unable to fly. They wander on foot around the colony, but still return to the nest to be fed. Eventually they make their way down to the rocks and attempt their first flight. Inevitably this lands them in the water, but the young birds find themselves swimming immediately with no difficulty at all.

The first sight of a cormorant in the water is somewhat startling. Instead of floating high and corklike as most sea birds do, its heavy body floats low in the water, with only a bit of the back exposed. Occasionally it sinks even lower into the water so that only the head and long snakelike neck are visible. The cormorant dives beneath the surface to catch fish. Underwater it swims with powerful action of its feet, holding its wings tight against the body as it pursues the silvery forms of fleeing fish. When at last the bird surfaces in order to fly, its tail and wing tips splash the water a dozen times or more before it rises clear. It is such a heavy flier, in fact, that, when leaving the island, it needs a height of land for an easy take-off. Even then its flight is downward at first, until the bird builds up enough speed to stay safely airborne.

Everywhere along the coast, cormorants are commonly seen sunning themselves, with wings outspread, on ledges, buoys, and channel beacons. The favorite resting place for the White Island cormorants is a long, low island of ledges, the Hypocrites, which lies in a somewhat sheltered area between the other islands of the cluster. Although the ledges are extensive when the tide is out, only a narrow ridge shows at high tide, and even this ridge is swept by the sea during every storm. Yet most of the time the barren upper ridge is lined with cormorants sunning themselves between one session of underwater fishing and the next.

No matter what its activity, the double-crested cormorant usually is easy to recognize. In flight it is somewhat gooselike in appearance. When it roosts, it often spreads its wings as it suns itself. When swimming, it usually rides low in the water with relatively little of its back exposed.

Seal ledges

The Hypocrites, strategically placed among the neighboring islands, serves seals as well as cormorants. The seaward end of the island is a natural rock harbor, at least when the tide is partly out, with boulders and ledges forming the shore. This is the home of one of the few remaining colonies of harbor seals on the New England coast. They bask on the rocks whenever they are not off swimming in search of fish and crabs.

Although truly creatures of the sea, as well designed as any cormorant for swimming underwater, the seals also are tied to the land as a place to rest and reproduce. The twenty-pound babies are born in late May or early June, and are soon taken into the water. Swimming comes easily to the pups, but since their endurance in the water is limited, they do most of their suckling on shore.

Even so, the pups are not reared on the island or even close to it. As soon as they can swim fairly well, they usually are taken up the nearest salt-water estuary to be weaned. There the waters are relatively quiet and safe, and as full of fish as the ocean, particularly when the alewives swim upriver from the ocean to spawn.

Altogether, the island group supports a close association of island creatures, all fishermen of sorts. Yet each goes about its business in its own way. The gulls dip to the surface of the water to catch fish. The terns dive into the water.

Its silvery fur stained with crude oil, a harbor-seal pup finds refuge on a sandy beach. Oil spilled by thoughtless seamen is a constant peril to marine life, for sea mammals and sea birds with oil-soaked fur or feathers often become so waterlogged that they die.

Bonaventure Island, three miles off the coast of Quebec's Gaspé Peninsula, has been famous for centuries as a sea-bird colony. Here gannets share ledges on the rugged cliffs with kittiwakes, common murres, and other kinds of birds, while storm-petrels nest in burrows on the island's summit.

The cormorants and seals swim beneath the surface. And the herons wade circumspectly along the island edges. Each lives on its own island, fishing as it pleases. And there is food and space enough for all of them to thrive.

The cliff dwellers

Mixed communities of another sort can be seen on a more dramatic scale on some of the truly great sea-bird islands. Perhaps the best known of these are two islands in the North Atlantic: Bonaventure Island, in the Gulf of St. Lawrence, and St. Kilda, off the western coast of Scotland. Less accessible but even more important are some of the islands farther north, including the Faeroes, Spitsbergen, Jan Mayen, Bear Island, Iceland and its satellite islands, the North American arctic archipelago, and even Greenland. Large or small, these islands of the North Atlantic and subarctic seas, which teem with fish and other forms of food, support enormous communities of sea birds.

The colonies on Bonaventure are particularly easy to observe, since the island lies within sight of the mainland near Percé, on Quebec's Gaspé Peninsula, and boats travel frequently to Bonaventure's small human community. Most of the high, rather flat-topped island, which is less than five hundred acres in extent, is covered by spruce forest. But bounded as it is by rugged cliffs, Bonaventure offers a wide assortment of places for birds to rest and nest.

Most of the birds live on the seaward side of the island, cut off by the forest from the half-dozen fishermen's homes on the opposite side. The seaward cliffs extend for a mile and are as much as two hundred feet high. Time, wind, and rain have carved ledges, crevices, small caves, and holes into their vertical faces.

Although several kinds of sea birds occupy the cliffs, no two species ever attempt to nest on exactly the same sort of cliff territory. All of them are fishermen, but each species

Percé Rock, between the mainland and Bonaventure Island, also supports sea-bird colonies.

The kittiwake spends most of its life roaming the oceans, far from land. It feeds and rests at sea and even is able to drink seawater. But in the breeding season it must return to the northern islands, where it nests on sheer rocky cliffs.

is unique in body structure, habits, and mode of living. Kittiwakes can build their nests on ledges only three inches wide, and these small gulls nest on the sheerest parts of the cliff. Murres, which are not quite so good at cliffhanging, nest on somewhat wider ledges and at the mouths of small caves. And the gannets, the most abundant of Bonaventure's birds, nest on the broadest ledges and on the slopes at the top of the cliff, where they are gradually encroaching upon the forest as their numbers increase. Right at the top are the little storm-petrels, which return at night to their nesting burrows in soft soil at the clifftop.

Kittiwake cliffs

The birds have not sorted themselves out so neatly on Bonaventure's cliffs as a result of mere chance. Each species has become adapted in various ways to occupy the differ-

142

ent kinds of available nesting spaces. The kittiwakes, for instance, are able to hold their place on narrow ledges because, compared with other gulls, they have unusually strong feet and claws. Their whole pattern of behavior, in fact, has changed substantially from that of other gulls.

Most gulls breed in colonies at open, accessible places such as the tops of islands. In such situations, the greatest danger is to the eggs and young. The adults can take to the air for safety in case of attack by predators, but in so doing they expose their nests to the raiders. As a result, the gulls typically have an alarm call that alerts all members of the colony to join forces to mob and attack intruders. Eggs and chicks, moreover, are well camouflaged, and the chicks are especially difficult to see when they scatter from the nest in times of danger.

For kittiwakes the situation is somewhat different. They build bulky cuplike nests of grasses, seaweed, and other debris, using mud to plaster the structure to the rocks on narrow ledges. The chicks, usually two to a nest, are not camouflaged and the adults rarely utter their alarm call, for there is little danger from land predators.

Murres, which share the cliffs on Bonaventure Island with

The common murre, which shares the cliffs on Bonaventure Island with kittiwakes and gannets, is not a particularly graceful flier. But underwater it maneuvers with ease, propelling itself by flapping its wings.

the kittiwakes, build no nest at all. Each female lays her single egg directly on the bare rock ledges. Since the egg is rather sharply pointed, it tends to turn in circles instead of falling off the cliff if it starts to roll.

The two kinds of birds are able to coexist on Bonaventure's cliffs only because their nesting requirements are different. The less plentiful murres breed on the wider ledges and leave the narrower ones to the kittiwakes exclusively. Although the two species do not compete with one another for space, however, individual birds must compete with others of their own kind. The cliffs can support only as many kittiwakes as are able to find suitable nesting sites, and the number of murres is limited by the availability of ledges of the type they require.

The life of the gannets

The large white gannets, with black-tipped wings spanning six feet, are surely the most spectacular of the birds at Bonaventure Island. They nest by the thousands on the island, and at almost any time great clouds of the birds can be seen flying and diving offshore. Like their tropical relatives, the boobies, they dive from considerable heights with wings folded back, plunging into the water like falling arrows. Although their dives are shallow when fish are near the surface, they are said to dive as deep as fifty feet below.

Because of their great size, the gannets do not compete with the much smaller murres and kittiwakes for nesting sites. They use only the broadest ledges and the flat areas

The gannets on Bonaventure Island nest both on broad cliff ledges and on open slopes at the top of the island. Following an intricate courtship that involves a great deal of bowing, billing, and posturing, each pair produces a single egg. The chick hatches in about six weeks, but cannot fly until it is fourteen weeks old.

on top of the island. On open slopes, they form large colonies with a distinctive arrangement of neatly spaced nests. Each sitting bird is separated from adjacent nests on every side by a distance just sufficient to protect it from the beaks of its neighbors. The best nesting sites, of course, are those closest to the center of the colony; nests near the edges generally are more exposed to predators such as herring gulls, which are always ready to pounce on any egg or chick that is left unguarded. These favored central nesting sites are so attractive to the birds, in fact, that in large colonies they usually are the first to be occupied. The early birds, in other words, get the first choice.

Plenty of food for all

Clearly, then, the different species on Bonaventure generally do not compete for space. Yet all of them are sea birds and all of them fish in the same general area. How do they avoid competition for food? A closer look at their habits reveals the answer. Just as each species uses some particular portion of the cliff and clifftop nesting territories, so each kind is to some degree a specialist in its choice of food and means of obtaining it.

Kittiwakes swim on the surface or may dive from the air, but usually to depths of a few inches at most. Gannets often dive from great heights and go deep in the water. Murres dive from the surface and maneuver with ease underwater. Each procedure results in the capture of food of a different kind, so that each kind of bird has a diet that is very much its own. As a result, there is always plenty of food for all.

A colony of several kinds of terns living on a single low island in the Black Sea provides an even more graphic example of how efficiently a community of sea birds can live together. In all, four species nest in the single mixed colony, and all of them cooperate in chasing away hawks. But each species feeds in its own particular way. One species, the Sandwich tern, flies well out to sea to hunt certain kinds of fish. Another, the gull-billed tern, feeds only on land, where it catches locusts and lizards. The other two, the common tern and the least tern, both fish fairly close to shore. But the least tern dives into shallow swampy places, while the common tern fishes farther offshore in somewhat

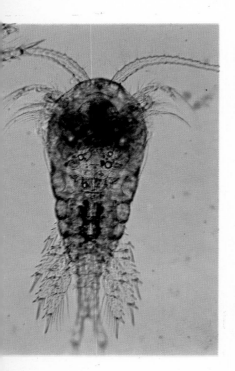

Copepods, tiny relatives of shrimps, are one of the myriad forms of life that drift near the surface of the sea. They feed on even smaller, microscopic animals and plants . . .

146

deeper water. Because each of the terns depends on a different source of food, the island, like Bonaventure, supports a greater bird population than it could if all the species relied on the same food supply.

Arctic islands

Throughout the Arctic, all sorts of islands support huge colonies of sea birds, for food is especially plentiful in these cool waters during the breeding season. In spring, with the increase in the length of day and the intensity of sunlight, the microscopic plant life of the sea, called *phytoplankton*, multiplies enormously. In turn there is an increase in the small marine animals, many of them shrimps or shrimplike in appearance, that feed on the phytoplankton. This is followed by the appearance of large schools of young fish that eat the shrimp and other creatures. And the shrimp and fish, in turn, become the main source of food for the breeding birds and their young.

With such an abundance of food, it is no wonder that the birds can thrive in great numbers. Enormous colonies of dovekies, gulls, and many other sea birds seem to flourish wherever naked rock stands clear of the ice and precipices rise high from the shore. On the eastern end of Baffin Island, for instance, tens of thousands of fulmars nest on the colorful rocky cliffs.

And then there are the murres and the dovekies, or little auks. These are the most numerous birds of the North, although it is uncertain which of the two kinds is more abundant. In any case, some of the islands off the coasts of Greenland are known to harbor at least several million dovekies, and at Spitsbergen black-and-white murres cover the cliff faces from top to bottom, crowding the ledges until there is room for no more.

On Bear Island, between Spitsbergen and Norway, unknown millions of murres nest on miles of cliffs that rise fourteen hundred feet from the sea. These are among the finest bird cliffs in the Northern Hemisphere, although some of the Aleutian and Pribilof Islands in the North Pacific probably support even more sea birds.

For abundance plus variety one of the finest bird islands anywhere is St. Kilda, lying out in the open Atlantic, forty

. . . and are eaten in turn by larger animals, including fish. The fish in turn are eaten by birds, such as this murre, and by mammals such as seals, or even by man himself.

147

miles from the Hebrides of Scotland. Although only about three miles long, St. Kilda has precipices that rise more than twelve hundred feet from the sea. About forty thousand pairs of fulmars nest on the ledges, and an equal number of gannets on surrounding islets make up the largest gannet colony in the world. And as many as three million puffins nest on the slopes above the cliffs.

Puffin cities

Puffins are a kind of auk, as are razorbills, guillemots, murres, dovekies, and the now-extinct great auks. With their neat black backs, gray-and-white faces, large, colorful, parrotlike beaks, and big red feet, puffins look like little clowns. On land, standing about ten inches high, they strut about upright like pompous little men. In the air, as they fly gracelessly about on short but powerful wings, they rather resemble overgrown bumble bees.

Puffins live only in the cold-water regions of the Northern Hemisphere. The horned puffin breeds on mainland coasts and islands of Siberia and Alaska, while the weird-looking tufted puffin breeds from northern California to northeastern Siberia and south to Japan. The best known species, the common puffin, breeds on North Atlantic islands from Maine to Greenland, Iceland, Scandinavia, and the British Isles. On the western side of the Atlantic an enormous puffin

During the nesting season, a puffin colony bustles with activity. At the left, several onlookers observe a pair of birds rubbing their bills as part of their courtship ceremony. In the burrow at the left, an incubating adult sits on its sparse nest of grasses and weeds. In the burrow to the right is a dark, downy, newly hatched chick. The immature bird at the entrance to the burrow is several weeks old. In contrast to the adults, it has a narrow, pointed bill. Among the birds at the far right are two successful fishermen, still holding their prey in their bills.

colony, with thousands of birds, is on Great Island, some two miles off the southeastern coast of Newfoundland. Although small compared with the three million puffins of St. Kilda, this is still a very large colony.

Great Island is a cold, hilly island shrouded in fog much of the time. A large part of the upper region is practically a bog, since the ground is soft and is forever collapsing as a result of the birds' continuing excavations. Although puffins occasionally nest in crevices, they usually breed underground after burrowing into the soil on the top of an island. They dig efficiently, using their heavy bills as pickaxes and their webbed feet as shovels. The completed burrow may be as much as five feet long and sometimes even includes one or two side branches.

This is certainly a sheltered way of nesting. By laying eggs and raising chicks in burrows, the puffins are protected from predatory gulls. Consequently the parents can safely leave eggs or chicks alone for long periods while they return to the sea for feeding and other activities.

Their underground colonies are faced by one great threat, however. On most islands that have been visited by ships, rats have established themselves and have become a severe menace to all sorts of birds, for they devour both eggs and chicks. In the case of puffins the danger is greatly magnified, since their burrows are ideally suited to rats, both as shelter and as a source of food. Once the rats take over, even a large puffin colony can quickly be exterminated.

Common puffins, among the most abundant birds of the North Atlantic, breed on northern islands from Maine all the way to the British Isles. They spend the winter on the open sea, and are regularly seen as far south as Massachusetts.

Unlike the breeding colonies of sea birds such as gulls and terns, which are in a constant state of uproar, puffin colonies are relatively silent. Puffins rarely cry out, but communicate with each other primarily by means of posture and beak movements. Although the heavy beak is primarily a tool for digging burrows and catching fish, its flaming colors seem to serve mainly for communication. Waving or jerking the head calls attention to the colorful bill and helps the birds in recognizing, courting, or threatening each other.

Puffins and other auks are very efficient fishermen that dive from the surface and catch fish crosswise in their beaks. Underwater they propel themselves with their stubby wings and use their large webbed feet for steering. At Great Island they have little need either to dive deeply or to stay under very long, for fish are so abundant in the nearby Grand Banks fishing grounds that plenty can usually be caught very close to the surface.

Puffins remain at sea throughout the long northern winter, gathered together in great floating rafts. How they live at this time no one knows, but as spring comes, the rafts gradually move toward shore. Finally the thousands of birds appear off the cliffs of Great Island, bobbing gently on the surface of the sea.

Raising the young

Soon the puffins begin to leave their floating fleet and
venture to come ashore. In the first flights ashore, the birds
land on rocky outcroppings, look about silently at their old
breeding grounds for an hour or two, and then return to
the ocean. But a day or so later they land for good and
begin hopping in and out of their burrows or stand about
gazing at any nearby activity.

Some clean out old burrows, while others walk in their
distinctive manner to visit other puffins. Some of the birds
gather beakfuls of grass and feathers, which will be incor-
porated in their underground nests. Pairs of puffins greet
each other here and there, mainly by slapping their beaks
together.

The single egg is laid in May and is incubated by both
male and female. The chick, which hatches by mid-June,
is covered with a warm, thick sooty-colored down. Once or
twice a day one of the parents flies in from the sea with as
many as a dozen small fish arranged crosswise in its beak and
plunges directly into the burrow to feed the chick. Soon the
chick is left alone more and more, and by mid-July it is
no longer fed at all. Their parental obligations now over, the

adults gather in groups along the cliff edges and sleep at night at sea.

The young puffins remain safe in their burrows, however, and acquire their complete winter plumage before leaving. Finally, about ten days after being deserted, they start to leave the nest. The young birds walk directly to the cliff edges and jump off, with their wings fluttering clumsily in their first attempt to fly. They usually reach the water unhurt and, once in their true element, immediately begin to swim, dive, and feed themselves.

Then the birds head out to the open sea. They will not return to the island until two summers later. Although they look over the breeding territory and poke in and out of abandoned burrows at the end of the nesting season, however, they themselves will not breed until the following year.

The greatest auk of all

Of all the puffin relatives, the most impressive was the now-extinct great auk. It was a large bird, standing about two and a half feet high, and looked and acted much like a penguin. Like all auks, it would dive from the surface for fish, using its wings as paddles just as penguins do. And like penguins, it could not fly.

The bones of great auks have been found on islands all through the North Atlantic, from the Gulf of St. Lawrence to the British Isles. They have even been found in caves that were occupied by Stone Age men, fifteen thousand years ago. Unable to fly from the men who slaughtered them for their meat and their feathers, the great birds gradually disappeared from island after island.

One of the largest colonies of great auks was on Funk Island, a lonely, inaccessible chunk of granite about forty miles from the northeastern coast of Newfoundland. This flat and treeless island, only a few acres in extent, is now inhabited by huge numbers of murres. But the only signs of

Although its bill seems ponderous, the puffin is an amazingly adept fisherman. Somehow the bird manages to catch as many as a dozen fish, one at a time, without losing its grip on the other fish already held crosswise in its bill.

Great auks, large flightless relatives of murres and puffins, once inhabited many islands in the North Atlantic. But the birds were so relentlessly slaughtered for their meat and their feathers that they were completely exterminated by 1844.

great auks are a few bones scattered here and there at the bottom of shallow lakes.

For more than two hundred years Funk Island, one of the auks' last strongholds, was dreaded by seamen as a bleak, haunted graveyard for storm-ridden ships. It was probably known by the Vikings a thousand years before, and plundered by the Beothuk Indians for at least another thousand years before that. Explorers, sailors, Indians, whalers, and cod fishermen have all reached the island, however. And all of them killed the flightless, helpless birds, which were easily driven into stone corrals from which they could not escape. The last of the great auks on Funk Island were killed by about 1800, and by 1844 the species was finally exterminated from all the North Atlantic islands.

Boobies mind their own business

Northern islands are not the only ones that support spectacular birds. Throughout the tropics two types of sea birds, boobies and frigatebirds, are frequently found together. Each in its own way adds a touch of grace and excitement to island life.

Boobies are closely related to the northern gannets and, as might be expected, are excellent fliers and superb divers. Frigatebirds, also known as man-o'-war-birds, were named after the elegant, fast-sailing warships of previous centuries. They cannot dive at all or even land on the water with any hope of becoming airborne again, but they are unexcelled in their mastery of the air. On land, however, both birds move about with difficulty, the frigatebirds hardly at all and the boobies in such a clumsy way that early sailors gave them the name by which we know them. In a striking way, the two kinds of birds greatly influence each other's way of life.

Boobies, the fishermen of tropical islands, live wherever they find the combination of suitable nesting sites and nearby water for fishing. Altogether there are just six species in the world; and three of the commonest—blue-faced boobies, red-footed boobies, and blue-footed boobies—are often found on the same islands, as in the Galápagos, mainly on the smaller, drier islands.

As might be expected, the three species differ in a number

154

of details in their life histories. J. Bryan Nelson, a naturalist who recently studied their ways, found, for example, that red-footed boobies incubate their eggs for an average of sixty hours at a time, while blue-faced boobies sit for about twenty-eight hours and blue-footed boobies sit for only eighteen hours at a time. In the warm tropics, such differences may not be important so far as incubation of the eggs is concerned, for the eggs are not likely to cool greatly when the adult leaves the nest. But they do indicate differences in the birds' activities, such as spending more or less time fishing or flying to and from fishing grounds. What we have here, in fact, is a fine example of how closely related creatures are able to live together by avoiding competition with one another. Each of the three boobies is a specialist in its manner of fishing and is unique in many ways.

Blue-footed boobies have an astounding ability to dive into extremely shallow water, even into water less than two feet deep. Since the males are smaller and lighter than the females, they can dive into very shallow water with hardly a splash. Thus, between them, they can fish in a

The blue-faced booby, one of three species nesting in the Galápagos, lays its eggs in a shallow depression on bare ground. The dark ring around this nest was caused by the incubating bird's droppings.

The red-footed booby is the
only member of its family that
nests in trees and shrubs.
Although its webbed feet are
adapted for swimming, the bird
can maintain its grip on
branches even in a gale.

greater range of water depths than either could alone. But,
male and female alike, they specialize in inshore fishing,
in areas where prey can be readily seen but where the
bottom is dangerously close.

A great advantage of their inshore fishing is that the
parents are never far from their eggs and chicks. They can
feed the chicks at frequent intervals, and are able to rear
two or three chicks at once. When the hatchlings are small
and need food at very short intervals, the lightly built males
make short, quick fishing trips. As they get larger and can
wait longer between meals, the females take over the whole
business, going farther to fish but bringing back more food
on each trip.

Red-footed boobies, in contrast, apparently never fish
inshore. Unlike the blue-footed boobies, they lay but a single
egg. And unlike all other kinds of boobies, which nest on
the ground, the red-footed boobies build substantial nests of
twigs in bushes and trees.

Since red-footed boobies fish in open water, often far
offshore, they are sometimes absent from the nest for several

156

days at a time, and during this time the young must go without food. Under these circumstances a single chick obviously has a better chance of survival, receiving all the food brought to the nest instead of having to share it with nest mates. Just the same, even the single chick has a hard time surviving when fishing trips are long and not particularly successful.

The blue-faced boobies, large, handsome, dazzling white birds, nest alongside either red-footed or blue-footed boobies. Like the gannets, which they resemble more closely than the other boobies do, they form colonies of regularly spaced pairs of birds. Such colonies may be seen far and wide on the small uninhabited islands of the tropical oceans. Each pair cares for one or two eggs, which are laid on bare ground. And just as their periods for sitting on their eggs are intermediate in length, they fish closer to their nests than do red-footed boobies but farther away than blue-footed boobies. Yet red, blue, or white, all the boobies are pestered by the frigatebirds.

As part of its courtship ceremony, the male blue-footed booby struts purposefully before the female. He lifts his feet high with every step, as if to show their brilliant color to best advantage.

Pirates and fishermen

Frigatebirds are perhaps the most acrobatic of all sea birds. Their wings are long, thin, and pointed, their tails long and deeply forked, and their bills long and hooked. They can soar like a hawk but also fly by flapping their wings when the wind is not strong enough to support them. They use their extraordinarily flexible tails for steering and braking and can adjust the sweep of their wings to swoop, soar, and dive with great speed. Frigatebirds, in fact, can fly circles around other birds, and often do just that.

On the other hand, they are not well waterproofed like other sea birds and therefore seldom if ever dive into the water or alight upon it. And unlike most other sea birds, their feet are only slightly webbed, having instead bare toes for grasping branches to perch on. The whole picture is one of a sea bird that rarely touches the water but is adapted for highly maneuverable flight.

On foraging trips frigatebirds may fly some hundreds of miles away from their home island, but they always return to rest. Sometimes they forage alone, although they often travel in groups of five or six. As they soar overhead, they are always on the lookout for fish schooling near the surface of the water. When they sight a school, they swoop down, sweeping just above the surface, and snatch the fish in their long, hooked beaks. Flying fish are a favorite prey. When frightened, they leap out of the water and skim along on outspread fins. Although they avoid underwater predators in this way, the flying fish are easy victims for the nimble frigatebirds.

The frigates are most famed as pirates, however, and often nest conveniently near colonies of boobies and other sea birds to practice their trade. They are so fast and well co-ordinated that even the simple act of passing food to the young is hazardous for the boobies. If the parent spills some food, a frigate may swoop in and snatch it before the startled booby can move. But the frigatebirds harass the boobies most of all when the boobies out at sea return from their

During the nesting season, the male frigatebird is an astonishing spectacle. On his throat is a fleshy pouch that can be inflated like an enormous red balloon. The display helps attract a white-bibbed mate and, later, warns intruders away from the nest area.

fishing grounds an hour or two before dark. Somehow the frigates seem to know when their victim has a crop full of fish. A mob of a half dozen or more may relentlessly molest it, even seizing the poor booby by the tail and capsizing it. They follow the bird's every turn until, in fright or desperation, it finally throws up its food. Usually only one frigate catches the thrown-up fish, while the others go off in search of another victim.

Although the frigates' piracy is spectacular, they probably do not cause much harm to the boobies or any of their other victims. A single colony of boobies may include as many as a hundred thousand birds; frigatebirds in the same area would not exceed a few thousand. In smaller colonies, the number of frigatebirds would be proportionately less. In any case, there is only about one chance in ten that frigatebirds will succeed in robbing any one booby of its fish.

Gliders round the world

Between forty and fifty degrees latitude in the Southern Hemisphere, fourteen-fifteenths of the globe is covered with water. Traveling westward around and around the earth is the current known as the West Wind Drift. Great surface swells progress westward over the ocean at about twenty to thirty miles an hour, creating updrafts and eddies of wind near the water surface. In these latitudes, known as the "roaring forties," the winds blow strong, are seldom quiet, and are often of gale strength.

This is the home of the wandering albatross, one of the largest of the thirteen species of albatrosses that roam the oceans of the world. As adults these magnificent birds have a wingspread of nearly twelve feet and weigh almost twenty pounds, though larger and heavier individuals are known. They may fly unceasingly for days at a time, but no one knows exactly how long they can continue flying without landing on the water to rest.

A Buller's albatross, a bird of South Pacific waters, soars effortlessly on long, pointed wings. True masters of flight, albatrosses can soar for hours at a time, alighting on the ocean's surface only to feed, sleep, or drink.

BLACK-FOOTED ALBATROSS

LAYSAN ALBATROSS

Two albatrosses occasionally are seen off the Pacific coast of North America. The sooty brown Laysan albatross nests only on the Hawaiian Islands. The more common black-footed albatross breeds on the Hawaiian Islands and on a few other central Pacific islands.

Theirs is not a flapping flight; indeed, their flight muscles are quite small, since they are needed only when the birds have no wind to depend on. The albatrosses soar and glide much like a sailplane, with only an occasional flap of the wings. Using updrafts from the waves to gain height, they swoop, bank, and sail effortlessly. Occasionally when there is no wind, they become water-bound and ride out the calm, sitting on the ocean's surface. When the winds begin to blow again, they take off by paddling to the crest of a wave, turning into the wind, spreading their wings, and simply allowing their bodies to be wafted into the air. But it is in a gale that they are truly in their element, flying and sailing with their legs pointing dead astern, and manipulating their long, narrow wings to gain the desired uplift or descent.

For the first few years of their lives, wandering albatrosses live far from land. Each bird travels alone, its territory the full distance around the globe, and in its early years it may circumnavigate the globe many times in its constant search for food. Where the water is turbulent, sea creatures are brought to the surface, and here the albatrosses feed. They do not dive, but instead swoop down upon anything that catches their attention near the surface and settle on the water to feed. Their feeding habits have made the wanderers famous among seamen. When a ship passes into their realm, one or two or sometimes several of the birds assemble around it, taking advantage of the food stirred up in its wake or thrown overboard by the crew. They sometimes follow the ship for days at a time before departing.

The great southern island

The wandering albatrosses continue to follow the winds and cold currents for the first five or six years of their lives. But when they become old enough to breed, they must find land. Late in the spring of the Southern Hemisphere, the birds return to a number of lonely, remote islands—Kerguelen, Gough, Marion, South Georgia, and the Macquaries, Tristan da Cunhas, Aucklands, Antipodes, Prince Edwards, and Crozets. Somehow, guided by changes occurring in its body as it matures, each bird apparently manages to find its way back to the exact island on which it was born but which it may not have seen since it first took flight.

Perhaps the most spectacular of all the islands is South Georgia, a mountainous island lying in the path of great gales that sweep unhindered around the world, beyond the tails of the continents. The island is long and narrow, with ice-covered peaks rising more than nine thousand feet from the water's edge and huge glaciers tumbling down the valleys to enter the sea. At lower levels there are steep, bare rocky slopes, flat areas covered with tussock grass, and many beaches.

South Georgia is no place for man, although a few people live with difficulty in a small whaling and sealing settlement on one of the relatively protected bays. But the island is a

Two Kerguelen fur seals romp in the snow on South Georgia. Although they are not nearly so numerous as they were in the past, about thirty thousand of the seals continue to thrive on the island's cold, bleak coasts.

163

The courtship display of the wandering albatross is an elaborate sequence of complex postures and ritualized movements. Throughout the ceremony, the birds accompany their movements with a medley of strange sounds.

safe breeding ground for animals that can tolerate the cold, cold winds. In addition to wanderers, species such as the yellow-nosed albatross and the light-mantled sooty albatross come to South Georgia to nest. And penguins, skuas, petrels, and seals—especially elephant seals—also breed on the island.

Old males, the first birds to return to the island, begin to arrive in late November. When the albatrosses come in to land, they are no longer masters of their element; they glide in with their great feet splayed out in front of them and, as often as not, crash-land on their breasts. For many of the birds, of course, this may be the first time they have ever made a landing.

Each male selects an old nest and drives off any of last year's young birds that are still hanging around. The nests are moundlike masses of tussock grass and roots, each one

about three feet high. They are built in areas of tussock grass on high ground, perhaps a thousand feet above the water, for the birds need a downhill run, if not a cliff, to get themselves airborne. Since the nests are situated in the open, the birds are exposed to the worst gales, which are fierce and frequent. But the winds also prevent too much snow from accumulating, and the breeding grounds are safe from burial when snowstorms come.

Black-browed albatrosses, the commonest and most fearless of all albatrosses, share South Georgia with the wanderers. Each year several thousand pairs nest among the tussock grass on the island's slopes.

Dance of the wanderers

Females begin arriving several days after the males. As each one lands, she frequently attracts two or three prospective mates, who begin to display to her. Each male stretches to

165

his full height, with his bill pointed to the sky and his wings spread wide, and begins bowing and braying as loudly as he can. Somehow the female selects one for a mate and joins him at the nest site.

Only then does the courtship proper begin. The wandering albatross, solitary and airborne for much of its life, has a remarkably elegant courtship ritual. With the male sitting on the nest and the female crouching beside it, they nibble at each other's neck feathers and utter an intimate duet. Then the male gets to his feet, stretches his neck, and makes a throaty sound as he starts clapping his bill. Following his example, the female stands and stretches, and the two birds fence with their bills.

As excitement between them continues to mount, the male stretches his neck high and points his bill skyward. With his wings spread and curved forward, he slowly begins to turn in a full circle, making noises all the while. The female walks around him, her neck stretched low to the ground. When the male completes his circle, he cocks his tail up and stretches to his limits. His display has reached its peak. The female copies him, and the birds face each other so that their breasts almost touch. This mutual display, now at the height of stimulation, usually culminates in mating. But whether they mate or not, such excitement cannot be sustained, and the birds sink exhausted to the ground.

This courtship dance continues on and off while the nest is being refurbished by the addition of new material to the old foundation. Once the single egg has been laid, the parents take turns incubating it for nine or ten weeks. Although one bird may be left on the nest for over a week at a time, the two birds usually change places more frequently.

Finally the white chick hatches out. For the first few weeks the parents guard it closely, but after about a month the chick is large enough to be left alone, and both parents go foraging for fish and squid. By May, as the Southern Hemisphere winter sets in, the young bird is still being fed, though far less frequently. The parents may stay with it for only a few minutes each day.

Protected by a warm coat of down and a thick layer of fat, the wandering-albatross chick remains on its nest throughout the first winter of its life. When it is nine months old, the chick finally grows its first coat of feathers and learns to fly.

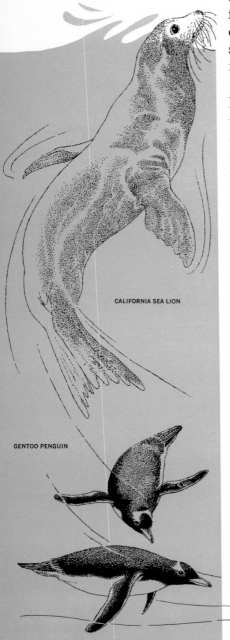

Oceanic birds and mammals have become adapted in various ways for swimming underwater. Some seals, such as fur seals and sea lions, use their large forelimbs for propulsion. And as with all penguins, the gentoo's wings have been modified into stout flippers, enabling it literally to fly underwater. . . .

CALIFORNIA SEA LION

GENTOO PENGUIN

By June the parents seem to abandon the chick completely, leaving it to survive on its own fat and to sit out the winter storms in the dryness and protection of its thick coat of down. In late winter the nests may be all but buried in snow, but still the young birds continue to sit. Perhaps the parents return occasionally to feed their young, as is the case with other albatross species.

The southern summer returns in October and November, but the only birds on the island are the young wanderers, now nearly nine months old. They are still unable to feed themselves, and have barely finished growing their first brown coat of feathers. At last, in November, they begin to fly, after perhaps a month of practice take-offs and flights only a few seconds long. With the onset of a new nesting season, the young finally abandon the nests and start feeding themselves.

They leave the island for good in the autumn, with the last of the breeding adults. For the next several years, sometimes as many as seven, they remain at sea, feeding in the circumpolar ocean currents. But eventually they, too, respond to a growing urge and return once again to South Georgia to start their years of breeding, spending nine months of every second year on shore.

Beachcombers

Birds that can fly to and from islands are not the only animals that use them as resting and breeding areas. They are also used by sea creatures that cannot fly at all. Turtles everywhere must lay their eggs beyond the reach of salt water. Penguins, like other birds, also must come ashore to breed even though they cannot fly. And so must all the sea mammals other than whales and porpoises, which bear their young at sea. All seals, whether they are known as sea elephants, sea lions, walruses, or simply seals, must come together on shore to mate and raise their young.

The most interesting of these flightless beachcombers are the seals and penguins. Unlike the other sea birds which can fly to high parts of the islands, the flightless penguins go only as far as they can walk. Many of them even have to be able to walk ashore, directly onto beaches, although some, especially the Adélie penguin, can zoom straight out of the sea onto ice or rock ledges several feet above the water. Seals of all kinds, on the other hand, are even less able than penguins to move about on land. They haul themselves onto beaches or rock ledges clumsily and with considerable effort. Even so, most islands with accessible shores are used for breeding by seals of one kind or another and, in the Southern Hemisphere, usually by penguins too.

When they come together on land to breed, some sort of social structure must be developed if large breeding colonies are to become well established. Sea birds have solved the problems of social life by forming small, close-knit families, with each family generally attending only to its own affairs. Seal colonies are social organizations of a very different sort.

Islands of seals

During the breeding season, certain kinds of seals set up a *harem system*, with mature males, or bulls, becoming very belligerent and trying to gather together and mate with as many females, or cows, as they can. The bulls are much larger, stronger, and noisier than the cows. There is no courtship, and the bulls have no bonds of affection with the cows, but simply assemble as large a harem as possible and mate with each member. Unlike the mutual cooperation of seabird pairs, this is a social system based on force and power.

This system for dealing with a crowded social life is well developed in the elephant seals, or sea elephants, the largest of all seals. Their name refers not so much to their great size as to the trunklike nose, or *proboscis*, that the male grows when he is mature. The male may be as much as sixteen feet long and four feet thick across his middle. His proboscis is often so large and floppy that it must get in his way while he is eating and even seems to make breathing a strain. The female is about half his length and less than half his weight, and has an ordinary seal's snout.

There are two kinds of elephant seals. The southern variety live in subantarctic waters and come ashore in spring to breed on much the same islands as the wandering albatrosses. During the winter they remain at sea in the rich waters of the "roaring forties" latitudes. When the whaling industry in the southern oceans began to be less profitable,

. . . Other animals, in contrast, use their hind limbs for propulsion. Cormorants occasionally use their wings when swimming, but rely mainly on paddling motions of their webbed feet. Certain seals, such as harbor seals, swim with alternating strokes of their hind flippers. When diving, they sometimes swim upside down.

DOUBLE-CRESTED CORMORANT

HARBOR SEAL

Basking beneath the arctic sun, a herd of walruses completely blankets the beach on an island in the Bering Sea. Males of these large members of the seal family may weigh up to three thousand pounds and reach twelve feet in length. Their tusks—actually elongated upper teeth—keep growing as long as the beasts live. The longest tusks on record measured thirty-nine inches. Walruses feed mainly on clams and other mollusks, which they find by diving as far as forty fathoms below the ocean's surface.

some hundred years ago, the whalers turned their attention to the elephant seals, killing mainly the huge males for the sake of their thick blubber.

The northern elephant seals suffered even more. At one time they lived and bred on islands off the California coast, from Magdalena Bay in Lower California to San Francisco Bay a thousand miles north. By 1900 hunters had reduced the population to one small herd on Guadalupe Island, 180 miles west of Lower California. Eventually the seals were protected by law, and today they are slowly resettling their old grounds—San Nicolas and San Miguel Islands off California, and Los Coronados, San Benito, San Geronimo, and Guadalupe Islands off Lower California.

Northern or southern, elephant seals are placid beasts, at least when not breeding. They have no fear, not even of man, and that is one reason why they were so easily killed by hunters. While they are fast and efficient in the water, they are clumsy and ponderous on land, and so they come ashore wherever they can move about without too much trouble. They haul out of the water onto sand or pebble beaches, or wherever there are not too many rocks, and hitch themselves slowly along on their flippers with great blubbery heaves.

Although the southern elephant seals leave their islands after they have bred and molted and do not return until the next spring, the northern seals often remain near their breeding islands throughout the year. They do not have to cope with the cruel winters of the subantarctic islands, but instead enjoy a yearlong subtropical climate.

An especially large colony is found on Guadalupe Island. The coasts are indented with channels, and lava flows of this old volcanic island have formed little coves and protected beaches that are ideal places for the seals to come ashore. Throughout the spring and summer, the seals sleep on the beaches, with few signs of any sort of social system. Their aggregations during the nonbreeding season appear to be quite random, in fact. The elephant seals seem to have a desire for animal contact and may even join groups of Cali-

The giant of the seal family is the elephant seal; a mature twenty-foot male of the southern variety may weigh as much as four tons. The inflatable proboscis increases the resonance of the bull's roar, which can be heard for miles.

fornia sea lions, a smaller, more active kind of seal. Occasionally they snort at one another in brief contests for favorable sleeping spots, but they are much quieter than the constantly barking sea lions.

The elephant seals show little aggression as they doze away the hours in closely packed masses, seemingly oblivious of each other and the more agile sea lions. Sometimes they walk over one another, and the sea lions may actually sleep on top of their larger cousins. Gulls and cormorants wander among and over them, and still they sleep undisturbed. At approaching danger the gulls almost invariably raise a great cry, which alerts the dozing seals. While the sea lions generally charge immediately for the water, bark-

At the first sign of danger, basking sea lions usually charge directly for the water. This stampede was photographed on Guadalupe Island off Lower California.

ing as they go, often the placid elephant seals simply raise their sleepy heads, ready to move to the water only if there is no alternative.

When they are not sleeping, the elephant seals usually are out in the sea, hunting for fish and squid. They fish alone, unlike the sea lions, which often leave and return to the island in groups of thirty or forty. The elephant seals can dive deep in their search for food and can see well underwater. They swim with their forelimbs pressed against their sides and the hind flippers pressed together. The hind flippers serve for both propulsion and steering, much like the tail of a fish, while the forelimbs are used for balancing, turning, and bracing against rocks.

Setting up a harem

Unlike the sea birds and sea lions that share Guadalupe Island and breed during the Northern Hemisphere's spring and summer, the northern elephant seals breed during the winter months. They become sexually active in December, at the same time that their subantarctic cousins begin to arrive at their breeding islands in the late spring of the Southern Hemisphere. Now a great change occurs in their behavior: their placidity disappears, and they become noisy and aggressive. The bulls are constantly challenging, fighting, and chasing each other, the pups squall, and the cows squabble continually.

The pups are born between mid-December and late January, the result of matings that took place nearly a year before. Although the pups will attempt to nurse from any seal of either sex, each cow is able to recognize her own pup and will not let any other cow nurse it. The cows are relatively careful not to crush the pups by accidentally rolling or walking on them, but the bulls are a serious hazard. A fast-moving bull will not turn aside for any ob-

On South Georgia, where the elephant-seal population totals about 300,000 individuals, an old bull dwarfs a nearby human spectator. Despite their fearsome appearance, elephant seals are rarely aggressive toward man.

stacle, be it pup or cow. As a result, the more crowded the colony is, the more pups are likely to be killed.

The pups get very fat on their mothers' milk. When they are about a week old, the mothers begin to leave the colony for a day or two at a time in order to feed, and the pups must fast during these periods. By about the end of March the pups are weaned and become independent, although they may wait another month or two before they enter the water and learn to swim.

Rearing the pups is only part of the story, for during the breeding season the colony is transformed from a random aggregation of sleeping hulks into a complex social system. Parallel to the water's edge there is an elongated, closely packed mass of cows, pups, and dominant harem bulls, surrounded by a line of subordinate males that lack harems but are constantly watching and waiting for their chance to acquire one.

Large, healthy, aggressive males, in their prime of life, take up the prize positions on the beach at the beginning of the season. The newly arriving cows congregate around these positions, and each bull concerns himself with maintaining his position among the cows. He is so truly dominant, so superior to the males that have poorer positions on the beach, that he seldom has to fight. He simply roars.

This is the season when the bull's trunklike proboscis comes into use. The dominant bull merely has to inflate his proboscis and roar at a challenging male. Recognizing the bull's strength by the loudness of his roar, the challenger usually gets out of range and scrambles into the water as fast as he can.

The life of a dominant bull is not very active or strenuous. He spends much of his time sleeping, roused only when another bull roars a challenge, and periodically mating with one of his cows. The only thing that really stirs him into action is the sight of a lesser bull attempting to mate with a cow in his general area. He immediately roars, charges at the couple, scares off the intruder, and proceeds to mate with the cow himself.

The dominant bulls seldom fight among themselves. They are of equal status and ignore each other completely. One blast of his trumpet announces a dominant male's strength, so that he rarely has to prove his dominance once he has established his position. Only early in the season, when the

HARBOR SEAL 5 FT.

NORTHERN FUR SEAL 7 FT.

CALIFORNIA SEA LION 8 FT.

WALRUS 12 FT.

ELEPHANT SEAL 20 FT.

Seals and their relatives come in a great variety of shapes and sizes, from five-foot-long harbor seals to twenty-foot-long southern elephant seals. Here the color bars indicate maximum lengths of adult males. Females usually are considerably smaller.

At the approach of a young male elephant seal, an old bull rears up to meet this challenge to his dominance over his harem of cows. The resulting contest may involve little more than roaring and threatening postures, or it could turn into a bloody battle that ends only when the challenger flees.

bulls first come to the beach, do the dominant males actually fight each other as they stake out positions on the shore.

But they do have to defend their positions from subordinate males that are old enough to breed but not strong—or loud—enough to maintain a position among the cows. These subordinate bulls ring the colony, with the strongest among them standing closest to the cows and trying to mate with any that stray a little. They are constantly fighting among themselves as they attempt to establish their relative dominance within the group.

Occasionally a challenging bull is not scared off by the answering roar of a dominant harem bull. When this happens, the two approach each other and then, with heads and necks held high and chests almost touching, proceed to lunge and bite at each other's necks. The losing bull, usually the challenger, soon flees, perhaps severely wounded by his opponent's bites along his unprotected back and sides. If neither of the combatants is a harem master, the fight may be long and bloody and may be carried even into the water. As a result, though most of the wounds are superficial, all the bulls bear scars from these encounters.

Also living near the breeding grounds are battered, decrepit old males. They probably were defeated early in the breeding season when positions on the colony beach were being established. These older, weaker bulls are not numerous, but their gregariousness and continuing desire to mate keep them near the breeding herd. Immature males and females that are not yet ready to breed also congregate nearby. The maturing males sometimes indulge in play-fighting, but otherwise the group remains sleepy and quiet.

By early spring, the new pups are weaned, the bulls finally lose interest in their harems, and the social system gradually breaks down. The adults molt and then return to their placid nonbreeding pattern of behavior. They simply sleep and feed and then sleep again, as they await the return of another breeding season.

Fur seals on the Pribilofs

Fur seals, close relatives of sea lions, also have developed a complex social system. Very large colonies are found on the Pribilof Islands, which lie in a cluster several hundred miles

CHANNEL ISLANDS NATIONAL MONUMENT

Rising from the sea off the coast of southern California are the eight ruggedly beautiful Channel Islands. Two of the smallest, Santa Barbara and Anacapa, were set aside in 1938 as Channel Islands National Monument, to be preserved and maintained in an undisturbed state for all Americans to visit, to study, and to enjoy.

Millions of years ago, the islands were connected to the mainland, but now they are separated by ten to fifty miles of deep water. Even though the islands are not so isolated as Hawaii or the Galápagos, however, the results of adaptive radiation are evident here too. In addition to at least forty-five endemic plants, the islands harbor a number of animals that differ from mainland forms and even from forms found on nearby islands.

But the greatest attractions for visitors to these uninhabited islands are the majestic scenery, the crashing surf, and the sea lions, elephant seals, and great flocks of sea birds that find sanctuary on these isolated outposts in the sea.

Like all the Channel Islands, Anacapa is girdled by tall cliffs, some of them more than five hundred feet high. In some places, the cliffs tower above narrow sandy beaches; elsewhere they rise directly from the sea.

181

Female elephant seals bask on the rocks on Santa Barbara's north shore (left). Visitors can expect to see California sea lions on the island as well. If they are especially fortunate, they may also sight the rare Guadalupe fur seal or even the nearly extinct sea otter.

Hikers wend their way up a path on Santa Barbara (right). The islands in the national monument have no permanent facilities for water, shelter, or utilities, but visitors can arrange their own transportation, bring their own camping gear and supplies, and explore the islands at their leisure.

Arch rock (left) is a famous landmark at the eastern tip of Anacapa. The picturesque little island's barren summit has served for centuries as a roosting place for flocks of brown pelicans.

north of the Aleutian Islands. The largest island, St. Paul, is about thirteen miles long; the smallest islands are little more than rocky ledges. On St. Paul, stretches of sand and broken rock along the shore alternate with cliffs as much as four hundred feet high. A few volcanic cinder cones rise from the top of the island, but most of the surface is rather flat.

In winter the islands are sometimes completely surrounded by ice, and they are swept by violent winds throughout the year. But in summer, when fogs and drizzle alternate with periods of sunshine, the islands are covered with lichens, and carpets of wild flowers suddenly burst into bloom. And in summer a million fur seals arrive to breed on St. Paul's twenty-mile shoreline, while as many more make use of the smaller islands in the group.

The fur seals select the rocky beaches or boulder-strewn ledges for their colonies, with each group usually isolated from its neighbors by a stretch of sand or a cliff. In many

Each year, sixty to seventy thousand northern fur seals —mostly young males—are harvested on the Pribilof Islands for the sake of their lustrous pelts. But the seals are protected by an international treaty, and the hunt is carefully supervised to assure a continuing harvest of the pelts.

ways their colony life is similar to the elephant seals', except that they breed in summer. And unlike the elephant seals, during the nonbreeding seasons they migrate far out to sea, some of them several thousand miles to the south.

Wherever they may be at the start of the breeding season, they all begin their long migration to the Pribilofs according to a particular timetable, and so the members of the fur-seal society each arrive at the proper time. Each spring the bulls push ahead to pick strategic spots along the shore. Later arrivals, the so-called idle bulls, take less desirable locations a little farther back from the sea and must wait until the beachmasters are tired of mating. Behind the idle bulls are the surplus bulls and the bachelors, the last to arrive at the colony. The surplus bulls move up when opportunities arise, but the bachelors are too young to mate.

During the six to ten weeks that the great bulls nearest the sea await the cows' arrival, they dare not even get food,

Summers in the Pribilof
Islands are brief and cool,
and as in winter, the
islands are often shrouded
in mist. Yet even in this
bleak subarctic climate,
the sun shines frequently
enough for plants to grow,
so that for a few weeks
each year the desolate
rocky meadows are
carpeted with a profusion
of blossoms. Mingled with
the cover of ferns, mosses,
and lichens are colorful
arctic saxifrages,
buttercups, asters,
gentians, geraniums, and
many other plants. Two
of the most conspicuous
wild flowers are the wild
lupine (*left*) and the
arctic poppy (*right*).

lest they lose their places. It is nearly midsummer when the females finally arrive, each one heavy with a pup which is usually born during the mother's first day ashore. As the cows come ashore, each seven-hundred-pound bull collects anywhere from three or four to forty or more of the docile little ninety-pound females. By August the harem masters are ready to retire and go fishing. It is now that the idle and surplus bulls have a chance to breed, for this is when three- to four-year-old virgin females begin to arrive by the thousands for mating.

By the end of summer the pups have learned to swim, and with the cold approach of winter they are ready to begin their long migration south. Many of the older bulls brave out the winter among the islands. The younger bulls travel a little farther south into dangerous waters, where some of them are eaten by killer whales. But the females, young and old alike, journey far across the Pacific Ocean to unknown destinations.

The world of penguins

In all, there are seventeen different species of penguins in the world. All of them live in the Southern Hemisphere, in areas where the ocean is cool and food is abundant. And all of them are expert fishermen and virtually fly under the water. Their bodies are streamlined for speed, and their wings, which are operated by great chest muscles, are hard and firm for beating against the water. Their feathers, moreover, make a dry insulating coat, and penguins are able to drink seawater instead of fresh.

But even if they can swim underwater as well as any porpoise, fish, or squid, once on land they have to walk or else toboggan on their breasts, for they cannot fly at all. They are, in fact, a race of short-legged waddlers. And while they have good underwater vision, their eyesight out of water is poor.

Of all penguins the rockhoppers, or jumping jacks, are

Rockhopper penguins are found on many subantarctic islands, where they build their nests of pebbles or grass on rocky shorelines. The most aggressive of all penguins, these two-foot-high bantamweights will even attack a six-foot human, jumping up to bite a sleeve or hand.

perhaps the silliest-looking species. With their puffed cheeks, crimson eyes, and shining orange-yellow crests, the rock-hoppers look half scared and half impish. They walk uncertainly, with feet lifted high, and instead of diving into the water, they jump feet-first off ledges.

Almost as ludicrous are the gentoo penguins. For unknown reasons, they cross perfectly suitable nesting areas near the sea on South Georgia Island and trudge wearily up the hillsides to make their nests near the tops of shelterless ridges. This may be an old habit carried over from the time, not very long ago, when only the rocky ridges stood clear of the surrounding ice. The gentoos apparently have retained an old instinct of ascending the ridges to find something more comfortable than bare ice on which to hatch their eggs. So up they go, raising feet high at every step and thrusting their heads forward to see where they are going.

The march of the Adélies

Perhaps the best known species are the Adélie penguins. Every expedition to the Antarctic has found them to be fascinating, inquisitive companions. The birds spend the cold, dark southern winter fishing and resting along the northern edge of the Antarctic's ice pack, but in spring they journey to their traditional nesting areas. Although many of the rookeries are near open water, some of the breeding areas are as much as sixty miles from the edge of the ice pack.

The long journey, made both by water and on ice, may last two full weeks. On the ice the Adélies travel as fast as a man can run, either by walking in short, quick steps or by tobogganing on their chests while pushing with wings and feet. When they finally reach their goal, the long lines of penguins break up and each male immediately stakes out his claim to a bit of land.

Once he has attracted a mate and the bonds uniting the pair have become firmly established, the birds begin to build

Adélies, the most widespread and abundant of all the Antarctic's penguins, are also the species most commonly seen in zoos. These friendly, amusing birds nest in rookeries that may be as far as sixty miles inland from the fringes of the Antarctic's ice pack.

their nest. They first scrape together a small mound of debris and then add pebbles to form a shallow cuplike structure. But even stones may be scarce in the Antarctic's barren wastes where the Adélies breed, and so the birds are continually stealing pebbles from their neighbors' nests. One scientist's attempt to test the Adélies' color preferences showed just how prevalent this sort of thievery can be. He presented the penguins with pebbles of several different colors, and before long the red pebbles, which the birds apparently preferred, began to show up in nests throughout the rookery.

Family life, once established, usually is faithful. Both

Adélie penguins build simple nests of pebbles on open ground. Other species nest in burrows, caves, crevasses, grassy fields, and forests, or, in the case of emperor and king penguins, build no nests at all.

parents take turns sitting on their two eggs. Each time they exchange duties, they go through a ceremony, rubbing their necks together and cackling softly.

Birds not on nest duty gather at the edge of the ice to frolic, chatter, and dive into the water to feed. Once in the water, they progress by "porpoising": they travel below the surface for ten to thirty yards, then shoot through the air in a seven- or eight-foot-long arc before vanishing again with hardly a ripple. When they have had their fill of shrimplike krill, they return to the edge of the ice and shoot out of the water like a jack-in-the-box, landing erect on the ice five feet above.

The Adélie penguin's chick, agile and active from the time of hatching, is covered at first with soft, dense down. By the time the chick is about seven weeks old, the down will be completely replaced by feathers.

Of emperors and kings

The large, handsome king penguins are found only on South Georgia and a few other subantarctic islands. On South Georgia Island they breed both on low ground amid the tussock grass and on bare, bleak moraines with snowbanks and glacial fields close at hand. Although king penguins incubate on bare ground, they act as if they were on ice; instead of making any sort of nest, the parent rests the egg on his or her feet and covers it with a fold of skin at the base of the body.

The chick finally hatches after an incubation period of nearly eight weeks. For the first thirty-five to forty days of its life, it is guarded constantly by one of the parents while the other goes off to feed. Before long, however, all the young in the colony bunch together in a large nursery, or crèche, where sheer numbers apparently provide protection from predators such as skuas.

Although large, the young birds in the crèche are not yet capable of catching squid for themselves. Instead they remain in the group throughout their first winter and are fed periodically by their parents. Surprisingly, the adults apparently can recognize their own chicks and will feed no others.

The closely related emperor penguins, which live near the edge of the Antarctic continent, have a somewhat similar life history. These birds, the largest of all penguins, stand as high as a man's chest and weigh as much as ninety pounds. Yet despite their great size they can shoot up from the sea and land feet-first on ice their own height above the water.

Like the kings, emperor penguins care for only one chick at a time. Strangely enough, however, the emperors not only endure the long darkness and bitter cold of the Antarctic's winter, but even use this season for laying their eggs and rearing their chicks. For about nine weeks in the coldest months of the year, the males huddle together in their rookeries, each one incubating the single egg that rests on its feet beneath an overhanging roll of fatty skin.

Like the proverbial "low man on the totem pole," an emperor-penguin chick peeps from between its parent's legs. The male incubated the single egg in this same snug retreat.

194

King penguins parade along a subantarctic island beach
at low tide. Although their markings are quite similar
to those of emperor penguins, the somewhat smaller kings
are only three feet tall and weigh from thirty to fifty
pounds. The emperors, in contrast, are the largest and
heaviest of all sea birds; they stand nearly four feet tall

and may weigh as much as ninety pounds. Despite many
similarities in their habits and life histories, the two
species do not compete for living space. The sturdy
emperors breed only on Antarctica itself, while the kings
are found on a number of subantarctic islands, including
South Georgia, Kerguelen, the Crozets, and a few others.

But the system has its advantages. The chicks hatch late in winter, and, with the return of daylight, grow rapidly in the brief spring and summer, when food in the surrounding seas is especially plentiful. With the next onset of winter, the chicks are fully grown and able to fend for themselves.

Worlds within worlds

Clearly, then, the penguins of the Antarctic are finely adapted to make the most of the special conditions on their own particular islands. The same is true of island dwellers everywhere. Just as boobies and pelicans are expert fishermen, frigatebirds are unexcelled in the fine art of pirating food from their hapless neighbors. And just as coconut palms produce large fruits especially well suited for floating from island to island, coconut crabs have evolved the means for exploiting this rich and plentiful source of food.

Yet interrelations of this sort are easily overlooked. Where the casual visitor to a colony of elephant seals sees only a random mass of bodies, the careful observer discerns an intricate social system. Through patient observation, scientists are gradually unraveling more and more of the secrets in the private lives of islanders.

You do not have to be a scientist to see these things, however. Any visitor who is fully alert to all the sights and sounds around him is certain to gain a deeper understanding of the lives of island plants and animals. And it is, without any doubt, the life of sea islands that makes these miniature worlds within the larger world of nature such fascinating places to visit and to know.

Just as seafarers long ago sought distant islands, vacationers continue to respond to the lure of sea islands. But the quest is no longer for material treasure. Visitors today seek an escape from the pressures of modern living and an opportunity to understand the life of these intriguing worlds in miniature.

Appendix

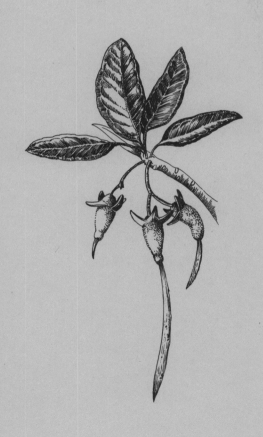

Sea Islands in the National Park System

Many of America's unique sea-island environments are protected today in national parks, monuments, and seashores maintained by the Department of the Interior. Including continental and volcanic islands, coral reefs, and sand keys, these publicly owned sea islands will be forever secure from exploitation and destruction.

A number of national seashores are located on barrier-beach islands, which are long, narrow, sandy reefs pushed up by the relentless action of wind and waves. Surf pounds the dunes and beaches on their seaward side, while the protected flank facing the mainland slopes down to salt marshes or mudflats. They are excellent places for bird-watching, as are the mangrove islands of the Everglades, the rocky crags off the Oregon coast, and the forested islands of Maine and Alaska. Most spectacular of the areas in the National Park System are the volcanic craters of Hawaii and Maui and the tropical coral reefs of Biscayne, Fort Jefferson, and Buck Island Reef National Monuments.

Although a curiosity about the natural history of America's remarkably varied sea-island preserves will make any visit more meaningful, the national parks and monuments are not reserved for the naturalist. In many of these sea-island parks, boating, swimming, fishing, horseback riding, camping, and even mountain climbing are encouraged activities for citizens enjoying their wilderness heritage. Detailed information about any of the parks may be obtained by writing to the Secretary of the Interior, Washington, D.C., 20240.

Acadia National Park (Maine)

This 32,000-acre park includes extensive spruce and fir forests, high mountain lookouts, jumbled blocks of pink granite hurled ashore by ocean waves, and hidden coves and tide pools that teem with sea stars, sea anemones, and other forms of marine life. From the summit of 1560-foot Cadillac Mountain, the highest point on the Atlantic coast, you can enjoy a panoramic view of the slopes of rugged, forested Mount Desert Island. Facing the ocean you can see Isle au Haut and the Cranberry islet group, while other islets in the Acadia Park group are visible closer to the Maine coast. The wildlife on all these islands is unusually

SEA ANEMONE

rich and varied, ranging from lobsters in the offshore waters to white-tailed deer on the mountain slopes. Camping facilities are provided on Mount Desert Island, but accommodations are also available in the island's resort community, Bar Harbor.

Assateague Island National Seashore (Maryland and Virginia)
Assateague, a typical barrier-beach island, offers sixty miles of broad, unspoiled beaches, dunes, and marshland. A great variety of marine life, marsh birds, waterfowl, and shore birds make their home on Assateague or pause here in their migrations. Well known for its wild ponies, the island now harbors an introduced herd of Japanese sika deer, as well as native foxes, raccoons, and smaller mammals. At the southern tip is a recreation area with protected beach. Visitors can follow nature trails at the adjacent Chincoteague National Wildlife Refuge. Maryland's Assateague State Park, toward the north end of the island, provides campgrounds and a beach for swimmers.

Biscayne National Monument (Florida)
One of America's newest national monuments, Biscayne encompasses a long, narrow chain of islands with coral sand on the ocean side and mangrove swamps on the land side. When fully developed, the park will provide facilities for underwater exploration in the shallow waters of its coral reefs. The islands lie close to the southeastern coast of Florida, but the Gulf Stream has carried here a variety of West Indian trees and shrubs not found on the mainland. The islands also are the northernmost outpost for several West Indian birds, including the white-crowned pigeon and the Cuban yellow warbler. The rare American crocodile is also seen occasionally. Just south of the national monument is John Pennecamp Coral Reef State Park, featuring spectacular coral formations.

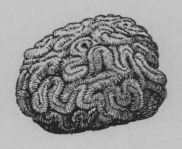

BRAIN CORAL

Buck Island Reef National Monument (Virgin Islands)
The outstanding feature of this unusual 850-acre park is the coral reef surrounding the eastern end of one-mile-long Buck Island, located a short distance north of the island of St. Croix. One of the few continuous barrier reefs found in the West Indies, Buck Island Reef is also considered by some to be one of the most beautiful coral reefs in the world. Snorkelers and skin divers can follow an underwater trail marked by directional and informational signs. Besides passing over magnificent stands of staghorn, elkhorn, stinging, and brain corals, visitors can swim among parrotfish, wrasses, trunkfish, surgeonfish, yellowtails, and other brightly colored tropical fish. Privately operated guided tours leave daily from Christiansted, the capital of St. Croix, where sailboats or motorboats may also be chartered. (See pages 22 to 25.)

204

Cape Hatteras National Seashore (North Carolina)

The Outer Banks, a giant elbow of sand thrust far out into the Atlantic, are famous for stormy seas, frothing surf, and hard white beaches. The national seashore is located on three islands: Bodie, Hatteras, and Ocracoke. In all, 155 miles of the islands' beaches and bay shores have been set aside for preservation. Gamboling porpoises occasionally are visible from the shore, and numerous game fish attract boatmen and surf fishermen alike. Behind the barrier dunes grow patches of loblolly pine, holly, and live oak and many species of wild flowers. On the protected bays and salt marshes facing the mainland, you can observe vast flocks of birds, including snow geese and whistling swans. Kitty Hawk, where the Wright brothers made the first airplane flight, and historic Roanoke Island are just north of the preserve.

SNOW GEESE

Channel Islands National Monument (California)

Anacapa and Santa Barbara, two of the smallest of the eight hilly, semidesert islands that are scattered for 150 miles along the southern California coast, have been designated since 1938 as Channel Islands National Monument. Herds of sea lions, elephant seals, and even the rare Guadalupe fur seals visit the rocky beaches of Santa Barbara, which lies thirty-eight miles offshore. Anacapa, ten miles from the mainland, is actually a five-mile chain of islets. Its sea cliffs attract nesting sea birds, and California sea lions and sea elephants often visit its shores. You can study many examples of adaptive radiation on these islands, such as the several races of birds and the forty-six endemic races of plants, including the giant coreopsis. (See pages 180 to 183.)

Everglades National Park (Florida)

Everglades National Park, America's largest subtropical wilderness, comprises over two thousand square miles of land and water at the southern tip of Florida. The park also includes countless islands in the Gulf of Mexico and shallow Florida Bay. Many beautiful and unusual birds find refuge in the tangled mangrove swamps of these islands. Some of the more spectacular species are the reddish egret, limpkin, Louisiana heron, little blue heron, white ibis, roseate spoonbill, anhinga, cormorant, and brown pelican. The country's only true stork, the wood ibis, also breeds on these islands. Boat trips to island bird colonies can be arranged within the park at Flamingo, where campgrounds and motel lodgings also are available.

Fire Island National Seashore (New York)

Fire Island National Seashore, a thirty-two-mile strip of barrier beach off Long Island's south shore, protects a threatened wilderness area not far from New York City. A special feature is the Sunken Forest, a low woodland of holly trees, black gum, and serviceberry. Growing among the dunes are thickets of wild rose, poison ivy, bayberry, and beach plum, visited in autumn by flocks of migrating birds. In summer the island has colonies of terns, piping plovers, and herons, and in the fall shore birds line the tide pools. Red foxes, white-tailed deer, and other small mammals can be seen on the higher ground behind the beaches. Guided nature walks are provided.

Fort Jefferson National Monument (Florida)
Administered since 1935 as Fort Jefferson National Monument, the seven islets of the Dry Tortugas lie seventy miles west of Key West in the Gulf of Mexico. Historic Fort Jefferson, begun in 1846, is a vast ruin covering most of Garden Key. Frigatebirds, boobies, noddy terns, and roseate terns are found on other keys, but the main attraction is the colony of more than 120,000 sooty terns on Bush and Long Keys. Green sea turtles still come in small numbers to lay their eggs, and the life of the coral reefs and shoals can be viewed by snorkelers and scuba divers. Visitors are welcome except in the bird colonies during the breeding season, but they must provide their own transportation, shelter, food, and water.

Haleakala National Park (Hawaii)
The large crater of the dormant volcano Haleakala on the island of Maui is the central feature of this national park, although a portion of the park extends all the way to the seacoast. Visitors can explore the crater along more than thirty miles of hiking and riding trails and can camp overnight in one of the shelters on the crater floor. The broad crater is studded with volcanic cones and recent lava flows of varied shapes and colors. In July and August silverswords bloom along the park road west of the crater and in the crater itself. In the forests on the lower slopes you can see a number of endemic Hawaiian birds such as the apapane, the iiwi, and the amakihi—all members of the Hawaiian honeycreeper family. (See pages 116 to 119.)

Hawaii Volcanoes National Park (Hawaii)
Nearly 350 square miles on the island of Hawaii are set aside as Hawaii Volcanoes National Park. Here visitors can explore a number of habitats, such as semitropical fern forests, arid desert, and the snow-capped summit of giant Mauna Loa. A storehouse of island endemics, the park is a protected sanctuary for silverswords, Hawaiian honeycreepers, and the endangered nene goose. But the park is most remarkable for its volcanic peaks and craters. The massive crater of Kilauea, in particular, has been noted in recent years for its frequent and often spectacular eruptions, and there are usually signs of volcanic activity. (See pages 116 to 119.)

GREEN TURTLE

Katmai National Monument (Alaska)

Katmai is a wild, remote region on the Alaska Peninsula, easily accessible only by air. Established in 1918, it includes over four thousand square miles of snow-covered volcanic peaks, glaciers, spruce forests, and icy blue lakes. The islets off the two-hundred-mile seacoast were added in 1942 to protect the sea-bird nesting colonies and the rich marine life of the Shelikof Strait. Puffins, auklets, petrels, murres, kittiwakes, and fulmars are among the birds breeding on the Alaskan coastal islands. From the mainland park the islets can be reached by floatplane or boat, and campgrounds are available on Kiukpalik Island. Nearby Kodiak Island, lying just across the strait, contains a national wildlife refuge of nearly two million acres, established mainly for the protection of the Kodiak brown bear and spawning salmon.

Olympic National Park (Washington)

One of the most picturesque areas in this mountainous park is a fifty-mile-long strip of Pacific coastline. Just offshore, though not actually part of the park, are numerous rocky stacks and islets that were isolated from the mainland by the erosive force of ocean waves. In spring and fall, small birds often pause to rest on the islets, and cormorants and other sea birds nest on many of the rocky stacks. These also serve as resting places for seals, which are often seen swimming just offshore. Fishing is permitted, and campgrounds and other accommodations are available in the park.

Padre Island National Seashore (Texas)

Padre Island is a typical barrier island arching 113 miles south from Corpus Christi almost to the Mexican border. The eighty miles of uninhabited coast preserved in the national seashore is the longest undeveloped beach remaining in the contiguous United States. Rising behind the broad sand beaches are dunes up to forty feet high, protected from wind erosion by tough-rooted grasses. Animal life includes coyotes, spotted ground squirrels, gophers, and even a few diamondback rattlesnakes. Surf fishing is excellent, yielding seatrout, redfish, black drum, and other game species. But the special feature of Padre Island is the large flocks of wintering waterfowl, including brown pelicans, white pelicans, herons, terns, egrets, and magnificent frigatebirds.

DIAMONDBACK RATTLESNAKE

Point Reyes National Seashore (California)

Point Reyes peninsula, an hour's drive north of San Francisco, is an island in the process of formation. The neck of land connecting it with the continent falls entirely within the zone of the San Andreas Fault: Point Reyes, slowly slipping northwest along the fault, will probably someday become a fully detached island.

The fogbound peninsula already has some island characteristics; for example, six endemic species of plants are found here. Inland are canyons and arroyos, forested ridges and grassy rolling hills. The area's most noted residents are the sea birds, including murres, gulls, and terns, which nest along the shoreline and on rocky islets in the coastal waters. A large herd of sea lions also frequents the offshore rocks and sea cliffs.

Virgin Islands National Park (Virgin Islands)

Most of the mountainous, lush green island of St. John and its offshore waters are included in the Virgin Islands National Park. You can explore highlands and ravines covered with hardwood forests and flowering plants such as hibiscus, flamboyant, and bougainvillea. Hummingbirds and even parakeets live in these moist forests, while cactus grows on some of the drier slopes. On the offshore reefs visitors can view corals, sponges, and schools of tropical fish. An underwater trail is marked at Trunk Bay for snorkelers and scuba divers, while other accessible coral reefs are found at Hawksnest, Leinster, and Lameshur Bays. Accommodations on St. John are limited, and reservations for cottages and campgrounds must be made well in advance.

SEA STAR

How to Make a Seashell Collection

Sea-island beaches are often excellent hunting grounds for sea-shells. Sanibel Island, for example, a barrier island off the western coast of Florida, is one of the world's most famous shell beaches, for many rare and beautiful specimens of shelled animals, or mollusks, are regularly washed ashore by the Gulf currents. But there are nearly one hundred thousand species of mollusks in the world, and they are widely distributed through cold as well as tropical waters. Even the beach nearest your home can be a good place to begin assembling a shell collection.

Looking for shells

A shell-collecting expedition requires simple equipment. You will need a pair of rubber-soled shoes for walking on slippery rocks and to protect your feet from sharp-edged shells. A stick for over-turning shells and prying them from rocks is also useful, and you will need a bag for storing specimens you decide to keep. In addition, you will want some small containers for tiny, delicate shells and a notebook in which to record your finds. Goggles and snorkeling gear are also helpful for underwater exploration.

The best time to go beachcombing is at extreme low tide when the maximum amount of shore is exposed. Walk slowly, examin-ing all piles of shells and debris. Look under rocks and seaweed, and even inside large shells. And wade into the water and search out underwater specimens.

The shore areas richest in mollusks are the zone between the normal high-tide and low-tide marks and the underwater area just beyond the low-tide mark. But don't neglect the upper beach areas either; after storms and hurricanes, the beach is often lit-tered with shells well above the normal high-tide lines. Protected areas such as sand and mud flats, tide pools, and shallow water

ANGEL WING
Cyrtopleura costata

SAN DIEGO SCALLOP
Pecten diegensis

209

are especially good places to look, as shells secreted by mollusks living in quiet waters generally are larger, spinier, and more intricate than those of other specimens of the same species living in rough, abrasive waters. When you find a shell you decide to keep for your collection, be sure to note where you found it.

Preserving and arranging the shells

Empty shells are more fragile and easily damaged than those still occupied by the animals that built them. As a result, your most perfect shells usually will come from live specimens. But you will have to begin by cleaning such shells before their tenants begin to decay. Put the mollusks in a pot of boiling water, boil them for about five minutes, and leave them in the water until it cools. Mollusks such as clams and scallops will open up and allow you to scrape out the dead animal. Other mollusks, especially snails, may be more difficult to clean, but any good handbook, such as R. Tucker Abbott's *Seashells of North America*, will give you special advice on the best techniques.

A handbook is also invaluable in helping to identify your specimens—often a difficult task as not all individuals of the same species look exactly alike. After identifying the shell, assign it a number and enter its scientific name and the number in your catalogue book—a loose-leaf folder with columns where you can list the species name, collecting locality, and other information. Also write the number in small print on the edge of the shell so that it can be identified if it is misplaced.

Many shell collectors keep their specimens in specially constructed cabinets with long, shallow drawers. These cabinets are designed so that one or more drawers can be removed to make room for very large shells. Although this is the ideal method for storage, the beginning collector can just as easily keep his shells in cigar boxes, egg cartons, or large cardboard boxes. But whatever method is used, each shell should always be stored in a separate compartment and wrapped in cotton or some other packing material to protect it against breakage. And each drawer

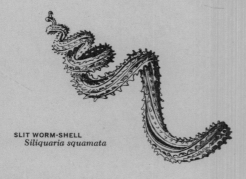

SLIT WORM-SHELL
Siliquaria squamata

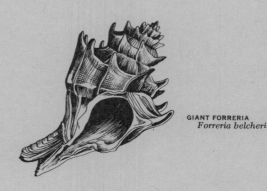

GIANT FORRERIA
Forreria belcheri

210

or container should be labeled with a detachable sticker describing its contents.

Your collection will be far more meaningful if the shells are grouped by family and species, with each specimen placed next to its nearest relative. This not only will make it easier for you to find individual shells as your collection expands but also will allow you to see at a glance which species you need to make your collection of a particular family complete. And it will form what amounts to a display of our knowledge of the evolutionary development of mollusks.

A scientific collection

Some shell collectors travel all over the world in quest of rare or unusually beautiful species. But even a collection made from a local beach can be valuable, provided it includes detailed, accurate notes on every specimen. There is still a great deal to be learned about the thousands of species of mollusks, and even the careful observations of an amateur can be of value to science.

When you first visit a beach, make a map showing the wind and wave currents, as the action of these natural forces can affect the development of a shell. Locate each shell you collect on the map. How far was it from the open ocean? Where was it located in relation to the high-tide and low-tide marks? Was it lying on the sand, half-buried in mud, resting in a tide pool, or settled in some other kind of habitat? When was the last strong wind or storm in the area? If you found the shell underwater, what was the temperature of the water? Was the water clear or murky? What other animals, sea plants, and algae were growing nearby? Compare the mollusk and its shell with nearby specimens of the same species. Are they exactly identical in markings and size? How do they differ? A careful consideration of questions like these will help you to understand the way that mollusks really live. Besides enhancing the value of your collection to others, it will also increase your own enjoyment and appreciation of seashells.

KELLET'S WHELK
Kelletia kelleti

KREBS' WENTLETRAP
Epitonium krebsii

211

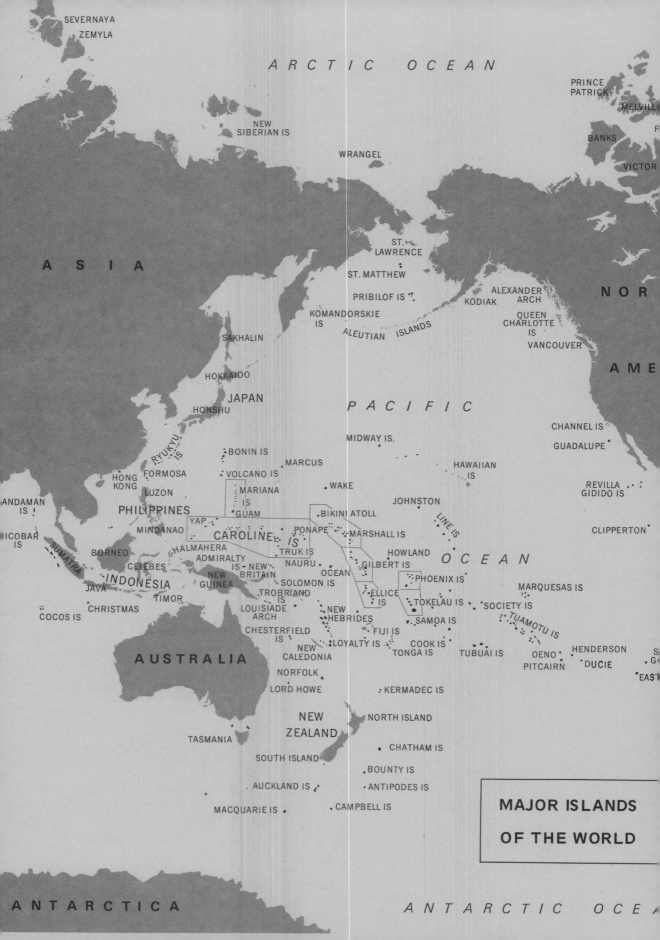

Endangered Island Life

It is hardly surprising that many island plants and animals are threatened with extinction. Some have always been exceedingly rare, and many are highly specialized in their habits. As a result, any rapid alteration of their environment, such as submergence of land areas, introduction of diseases, or changes brought about by man, can prove fatal; if the change takes place faster than evolutionary processes, the plants and animals simply do not have time to adapt to the new living conditions. For some species, the destruction of a single marsh, forest, or food source can spell doom.

Man, of course, has been the greatest single destroyer of islands and their inhabitants. Sometimes he kills the animals themselves for the sake of their flesh, fur, or feathers. He also introduces new animals such as goats, which compete with the island spe-

CRESTED HONEYCREEPER
For many years, Hawaii's crested honeycreeper was thought to be extinct. At one time it lived in mountain forests on both Molokai and Hawaii. And then it vanished. But in recent years this little black bird with orange-red markings and a jaunty crest has been very rarely seen or heard in high mountain rain forests on Maui. Diseases brought in with introduced birds and destruction of its habitat have both played a role in its decimation.

PUERTO RICAN PARROT
Although once widely distributed in Puerto Rico, these handsome, one-foot-long parrots have been nearly eliminated from the island. Destruction of forests, lack of suitable nesting holes in trees, and predation by rats and other animals all seem to have contributed to its decline. Now fewer than two hundred of the birds remain, all within the Caribbean National Forest. Complete protection and further studies of its habitat and food requirements offer the parrot's only prospect for survival.

cies for food, and others such as rats, mongooses, and house cats, which prey on the native islanders. Worse still is man's own penchant for altering or totally destroying habitats, whether by cutting forests, by draining marshes, by covering coral islets with landing strips, or by other means. Finally and most recently, he has begun polluting land and sea with dangerous chemicals.

Many island species, such as the dodo, the great auk, and twenty-two unique species of Hawaiian birds, already are extinct. Yet others can be saved. Man can be a constructive influence as well as a destructive one. Some endangered animals can be bred in captivity and their offspring released in the wild, as has been done with Hawaii's famous goose, the nene. Others, like the sea otter and northern fur seal, can be saved simply through strict enforcement of protective legislation. Most important of all, man can protect and restore areas of native habitat in refuges, sanctuaries, and state and national parks and forests.

But time is running short for many of the endangered island species. If they are to be saved from extinction, we must act now.

BERMUDA PETREL

When Bermuda was first discovered, thousands of these birds nested on the island. But the ravages of introduced pigs and rats were so thorough that, for three centuries, the petrels were thought to be extinct. In 1951, however, a tiny remnant population was rediscovered on offshore islets. Under complete protection, the birds increased in numbers for several years, but now they seem to be in trouble again. Apparently pollution of the sea with DDT is causing a decline in fertility of their eggs.

IPSWICH SPARROW

This rare grayish sparrow is threatened not so much by the actions of man as by the forces of nature. It breeds only on Sable Island off the coast of Nova Scotia, and this small island is slowly disappearing into the sea. If the time ever comes when the sea completely inundates the island, the bird will be doomed. Its wintering grounds—beaches and dunes along the Atlantic Seaboard—on the other hand, seem fairly secure as more and more dune habitat is protected in national seashores and state parks.

GUADALUPE FUR SEAL

These seals once flourished on islands off California, but sealers slaughtered so many that by 1900 they were all but extinct. In 1954, however, a small colony was discovered on Guadalupe Island off the coast of Lower California and, under strict international protection, their numbers are gradually increasing. By 1965, the population was estimated to number about six hundred. Now, on rare occasions, they are sighted even in the waters around Channel Islands National Monument.

CUBAN CROCODILE

Once widespread in Cuban swamps and marshes, this unique species seems to have been the victim of habitat destruction and excessive hunting for its hide. Fewer than five hundred Cuban crocodiles remain alive in a tiny area of undisturbed wetland in Zapata Swamp and perhaps in a few other places. Part of the swamp is now preserved as a crocodile refuge, where the animals are carefully protected, and a number of specimens are being kept in zoos.

KERGUELEN CABBAGE

This strange plant is just one of many unique island species that are threatened with extinction. Found only on windswept, subantarctic Kerguelen Island, it grows large cabbagelike rosettes of leaves and produces tall stalks of wind-pollinated flowers. Depredation by grazing animals seems to be partly responsible for its increasing rarity, but like other island species, it probably also is suffering from competition with introduced plants.

216

The Sea-bird Families

While many families of birds may be found near or along sea-coasts or on sea islands, only those birds that actually spend most of their time on or over salt water can rightfully be considered sea birds. The oystercatchers and other shore birds that frequent beaches and rocky shores, for example, are not true sea birds, nor are the herons, spoonbills, and flamingos that live on the shores of bays, marshes, and salt creeks. But the cormorants and murres that nest on cliffs over crashing surf and feed on the oceans and bays are sea birds. Truest of all sea birds are the pelagics—those species, including shearwaters, albatrosses, petrels, skuas, and boobies, that spend all their days during the nonbreeding season out of sight of land, roaming the ocean wilderness. Distinctive features of each family of sea birds are described here.

Penguins—Spheniscidae

All seventeen species of penguins live in the Southern Hemisphere, breeding on Antarctica and surrounding islands, on the southern coasts of Africa, Australia, and New Zealand, and north along the Pacific coast of South America to the Galápagos Islands. These familiar black-and-white birds range in size from the sixteen-inch-long little penguin to the four-foot-long emperor penguin. All species have short tails, webbed feet, and dense plumage. On land these flightless birds waddle upright or toboggan on their bellies. But in the water they are swift and agile swimmers, propelling themselves beneath the surface with wings that have been modified into paddlelike flippers. Penguins lay their eggs on the ground, in burrows, or in caves, and in some cases incubate the eggs between the feet under an abdominal fold of skin.

MAGELLANIC PENGUIN

Albatrosses—Diomedeidae

The albatrosses, like birds of several closely related families (the shearwaters, storm-petrels, and diving petrels), are unique in having nostrils that extend onto the bill in short tubes. Albatrosses range all the oceans of the world but are concentrated in southern seas, particularly in the Pacific. There are fourteen species, of which six are found around North America. Albatrosses glide on long, pointed wings as they roam the open seas, often following ships, and come ashore only to nest. Most are colonial breeders and have elaborate courtship displays. The single egg is usually laid on bare ground. Albatrosses feed on many forms of marine

YELLOW-NOSED ALBATROSS

life, which the birds capture at or just below the surface of the water.

Petrels, Shearwaters, and Fulmars—Procellariidae

FULMAR

These birds, which are closely related to albatrosses, have nostrils in short tubes on the upper side of the bill. The family includes fifty-six species, with plumages mainly in shades of black, brown, gray, and white. Most shearwaters and petrels live in the Southern Hemisphere, but a number are found in northern waters in summer; the fulmar lives only in the Northern Hemisphere. These far-ranging marine birds characteristically fly on stiff wings just above the waves, and migrate vast distances each year. They skim food from the ocean's surface or, more rarely, feed while sitting on the water. They are gregarious birds, normally breeding in colonies. The nests, in rock crevices or burrows, contain a single egg.

Storm-petrels—Hydrobatidae

WILSON'S PETREL

Storm-petrels are the smallest of the tube-nosed ocean rovers; the eighteen species in the family range from five and one-half to ten inches in length. Most are dark-brown, black, or gray, with white rumps. All have an erratic, fluttering, batlike flight and feed on plankton from the surface of the sea. Storm-petrels are the so-called Mother Carey's chickens that commonly follow ships on the open ocean. But they rarely pursue ships into harbors, and come ashore only to nest. They breed in colonies, with each pair caring for a single egg in its nest in a burrow or rock crevice. Seven species of storm-petrels are found in ocean waters around the United States.

Diving Petrels—Pelecanoididae

PERUVIAN DIVING PETREL

Unlike other petrels, these unusual little sea birds dive for their food. All five species live along the coasts of Southern Hemispheric oceans. They are chunky and small (seven to ten inches long), with black backs and white underparts. Their nostrils are enclosed in tubes on the upper side of the bill. The birds fly with rapid wing beats and, like the auks, use their wings for propulsion underwater. Diving petrels are colonial breeders, with each pair producing a single white egg in a burrow dug into soft earth.

Tropicbirds—Phaethontidae

Although they are not closely related to terns, the handsome, graceful tropicbirds look and act like large terns with long, streaming central tail feathers. They are found over tropical seas around the world and breed on ledges of sea cliffs. Tropicbirds make no nest, but instead lay their single egg on bare rock or earth. All three species are white marked with black; one species has long vermilion tail feathers. Tropicbird feeding habits are ternlike; the birds range far out to sea in search of small fish, then plummet down with folded wings, striking the water with a splash. On land they can only shuffle.

YELLOW-BILLED TROPICBIRD

Pelicans—Pelecanidae

Pelicans are members of an ancient family, with six living species widely scattered around the world. They are long-necked, bulky birds with capacious pouches on the undersides of their bills. Most species are white or shades of gray; the brown pelican of the New World is an exception. Pelicans often inhabit inland lakes and other bodies of water, but many spend part of the year along seacoasts. Sometimes they fish while swimming on the surface, but they also dive from the air, flopping awkwardly into the water with wings half-open. They are colonial birds, with each pair producing one to four young in nests that are sometimes built in trees or low shrubs, but usually are built on the ground.

BROWN PELICAN

Gannets and Boobies—Sulidae

Gannets and boobies are among the master fishermen of the bird world. They plummet from considerable heights, hitting the water with great impact, and can dive as deep as one hundred feet beneath the surface in pursuit of their prey. Boobies live in the tropics, while gannets belong to the cold waters of the world. All nine species are goose-sized birds that fly with powerful wing beats and short glides. Some species are black and white; others are combinations of brown and white. All species are highly gregarious and live in vast colonies, where each mated female lays one to three eggs.

GANNET

Cormorants—Phalacrocoracidae

Thirty species are included in this family of large, strong-tailed birds with snakelike necks and long, hooked bills. Coloration is predominantly black, with bright bare skin on the face. Cormorants are found all around the world on islands, along seacoasts, and inland, but they rarely stray far out over the ocean. These superb fishermen dive from the surface and swim underwater, often in groups, to pursue and catch their prey. Cormorants nest in colonies. Each nest, a pile of debris built either on the ground or in a tree, usually contains two to four eggs.

Frigatebirds—Fregatidae

All five species of frigatebirds are confined to tropical seacoasts and islands. Both sexes are brown-black with some iridescence in

BRANDT'S CORMORANT

MAGNIFICENT FRIGATEBIRD

COMMON EIDER

NORTHERN PHALAROPE

POMARINE JAEGER

the plumage. Males have throat sacs that are inflated during courtship and territorial displays. With long wings and deeply forked tails, frigatebirds are masters of effortless soaring. They obtain most of their food by harassing other sea birds as they return from fishing expeditions; they force their victims to drop their catch in midair, then swoop down and snatch the fish for themselves. Also known as man-o'-war-birds, frigatebirds nest in colonies, either in bushes or on the ground. Each pair normally raises only one chick.

Swans, Geese, and Ducks—Anatidae

Many of the 145 species of waterfowl in this family are true sea birds that spend most of their lives along the seacoasts of the world. Among the American sea ducks are the eiders, the scoters, the harlequin duck, and the oldsquaw duck. Birds in this family vary greatly in size and coloration, but all have broad, flat bills, relatively short legs, and webbed feet. They feed either by diving below the surface of the water or, in the case of some fresh-water species, by dabbling—tipping the body forward and extending only the head and neck underwater. The birds eat a variety of plants as well as small water animals. Most species are migratory. Nests and number of eggs vary widely.

Phalaropes—Phalaropodidae

Of all the shore birds, only the phalaropes are true seafarers. All three species in the family breed in arctic and subarctic regions and migrate across open ocean to the tropics, with two of the species wintering at sea. When feeding, they alight on the surface of the water in large groups and circle or spin like tops as they snatch insects and small crustaceans. Phalaropes are robin-sized or smaller, and have needlelike bills. Females have more colorful patterns than the males. They nest on the ground, usually laying four eggs, which the male incubates.

Skuas—Stercorariidae

In Great Britain, all species in this pelagic family are known as skuas, but in America three of the four species are called jaegers. They breed in high latitudes, ranging close to both poles, and migrate long distances annually. Coloration is brown or black, with lighter undershadings in some plumages. These "sea hawks" are swift and powerful predators, favoring the eggs and young of other sea birds, as well as small mammals and carrion. They are also adept at robbing other sea birds of their catch. Skuas nest in or near the colonies of other birds, and each female lays two to four eggs in a depression in the grass.

Gulls and Terns—Laridae

This large worldwide family is divided into two subfamilies, one including the forty-three species of gulls and the other the thirty-nine species of terns. Gulls are generally heavier-bodied and slower in flight than terns, although there are dainty gulls and bulky terns. Terns have slender, pointed bills; gulls' bills are stouter and slightly hooked. Typical coloration for both subfamilies is a combination of gray above with black on the wings and white below. Immature gulls are often feathered in shades of brown. Most species are migratory, except for residents of the tropics. Gulls and terns nest in colonies along seacoasts or in inland areas. The average clutch includes one to four eggs.

GREAT BLACK-BACKED GULL

Skimmers—Rynchopidae

Skimmers are short-legged, long-winged, ternlike birds that live along seacoasts, although many are also found along inland rivers. They are black, brown, or slate-colored above and white below. The skimmer's knifelike bill is higher than it is wide, and the lower mandible is considerably longer than the upper one. This enables the skimmer to feed by flying just above the water with its mouth open so that the lower mandible actually plows the surface as the bird scoops up small fish and crustaceans. Skimmers nest on sandy beaches, laying two to five eggs per nest. The family includes three species, but only the black skimmer is found in North America.

BLACK SKIMMER

Auks, Murres, and Puffins—Alcidae

This family includes twenty-two subarctic species, with such varied names as auk, auklet, murre, murrelet, puffin, guillemot, and dovekie. The birds range in size from the six-and-one-half-inch-long least auklet to the seventeen-inch-long common murre, although the now-extinct great auk measured thirty inches long. All species are compact, short-necked sea birds with large webbed feet, legs set far back on the body, and stubby wings that assist in swimming underwater. Their bills are adapted for fishing in various ways. Coloration is generally black or gray with areas of white. These birds are colonial, nesting in rock crevices or in burrows, and producing one or two young per pair.

DOVEKIE

Glossary

Adaptation: An inherited structural, functional, or behavioral characteristic that improves an organism's chances for survival in a particular *habitat*. *See also* Specialization.

Adaptive radiation: The evolution of closely related organisms into strikingly different forms as they become adapted to, different modes of life or different environmental conditions.

Air plant: *See* Epiphyte.

Alga (plural *algae*)**:** The simplest of all plant forms, having neither roots, stems, nor leaves. Algae range in size from microscopic single cells to branching forms one hundred feet or more in length.

Annual: A plant that completes its life cycle from seedling to mature seed-bearing plant during a single growing season, then dies.

Archipelago: A group or cluster of many islands.

Atoll: A ring-shaped chain of *coral islands* and reefs enclosing or partly enclosing a shallow *lagoon*.

Barrier island: A long, narrow island parallel to and not far from a mainland coast. The island is composed of material heaped up by ocean waves and currents. A barrier island typically has open beaches on the ocean side, sand dunes down its spine, and shallow marshy areas on the mainland side.

Biologist: A scientist who specializes in the study of living organisms.

Bract: A specialized leaf growing at the base of a flower or cluster of flowers.

Carapace: A hard, shell-like covering on the upper side of an animal's body, such as the upper shell of a crab or turtle.

Carnivore: An animal that lives by eating the flesh of other animals.

Climate: The average weather conditions of an area, including temperature, rainfall, humidity, wind, and hours of sunlight, based on records kept for many years.

Cold-blooded: Lacking the ability to regulate body temperature, with the result that body temperature fluctuates substantially with variations in external temperature. *See also* Warm-blooded.

Colonization: The occupation of living space by organisms that had not previously lived there.

Community: All the plants and animals in a particular *habitat* that are bound together by feeding habits and other interrelations.

Competition: The struggle between individuals or groups of individuals for common necessities such as water, food, and living space.

Conifer: A plant that bears its seeds in cones. Pines, spruces, and firs are well-known conifers.

Conservation: The use of natural resources in a way that assures their continuing availability to future generations; the wise use of natural resources.

Continent: One of the seven great land masses on the earth. The continents are Africa, Antarctica, Asia, Australia, Europe, North America, and South America. *See also* Island.

Continental island: An island that was originally part of a *continent* but was cut off by forces such as water erosion, rising sea level, or gradual submergence of a portion of the continent. *See also* Oceanic island.

Coral: Any of a group of small marine animals characterized by an ability to secrete stony external skeletons. Individual coral animals are called *polyps*. Most species live in colonies that grow in various elaborate forms.

Coral island: An island formed of masses of the stony skeletons of coral colonies or of sand composed of coral fragments.

Coral reef: A *reef* formed by coral growing in shallow water. A coral reef may be continuously submerged or it may be exposed by each low tide.

Crèche: A group of immature birds of more or less the same age that gather together for protection in a breeding colony. Young penguins and flamingos typically gather in crèches.

Crustacean: A member of the large group of animals that includes lobsters, crabs, amphipods, copepods, and similar forms. Crustaceans are characterized by jointed legs, segmented bodies, and hard external skeletons.

Dispersal: The actual movement of plants, animals, seeds, or eggs from one place to another. Many organisms have intricate adaptations assuring their dispersal into new areas.

Display: An inherited behavior pattern, often involving elaborate posturing, movements, or other ritualized actions, by which animals communicate with others of the same species. Displays are usually associated with activities such as courtship and territorial defense.

Ecology: The scientific study of the relationships of living things to one another and to their *environment*.

Endemic: Referring to a plant or animal *species* that occurs naturally only in a restricted geographical area, such as on an island or group of islands, and is found nowhere else unless it has been transplanted.

Environment: All the external conditions, such as soil, water, air, and climate, surrounding a living thing.

Epiphyte: A plant that grows upon or attached to another plant or some nonliving support but derives no sustenance from the supporting structure. Epiphytes are often called air plants.

Erosion: The wearing away of areas of the earth's surface by water, wind, ice, and other natural forces.

Evolution: The process of natural consecutive modification in the inherited makeup of living things; the process by which modern plants and animals have arisen from forms that lived in the past.

Fossil: Remains or traces of animals or plants that lived in the prehistoric past, whether bone, cast, track, imprint, pollen, or any other evidence of their existence.

Geologist: A scientist who specializes in the study of the earth and the rocks that form it.

Geyser: A hot spring that emits jets of water or steam in intermittent bursts.

Guano: Excrement, as of bats or sea birds. In certain bat caves and on islands colonized by sea birds, guano sometimes accumulates in such vast quantities that it is mined commercially for fertilizer.

Habitat: The immediate surroundings (living place) of a plant or animal; everything necessary to life in a particular location except the life itself.

Harem system: The social system of certain animals, such as elephant seals, in which a group of females (the harem) is dominated during the breeding season by a single male and mate only with that male.

Incubation: The act of maintaining the temperature of an egg by external means in order that the embryo within may develop and hatch.

Intertidal zone: The area along a coastline which is alternately covered by water and exposed to air because of the rise and fall of tides.

Invertebrate: An animal without a backbone; one of the so-called lower animals, such as worms, insects, and *crustaceans*.

Island: A body of land, smaller than a *continent*, completely surrounded by fresh or salt water.

Key (also spelled *cay*): A low *island* or *reef*, such as the small islets off the southern coast of Florida.

Lagoon: The shallow body of water within a coral *atoll*.

Larva (plural *larvae*): An active, immature stage in an animal's life history, during which its form differs from that of the adult. The caterpillar, for example, is the larval stage in the life history of a butterfly; the tadpole is the larva of a frog.

Lava: The molten rock flowing from a *volcano* or fissure in the earth's crust; the rock formed by the cooling of this material.

Mammal: A member of the group of animals including humans, rodents, bats, and many other forms. All are *warm-blooded*, possess special milk-producing glands, are at least partially covered by hair, and usually bear their young alive.

Marsupial: A *mammal*, such as an opossum or kangaroo, that bears its young in a relatively undeveloped stage and carries them for a time after birth in an external abdominal pouch.

Megalops: A late larval stage in the development of certain *crustaceans*. The megalops resembles the adult more closely than does the earlier *zoea* stage.

Migration: A periodic, especially seasonal or annual, movement from one place to another of large numbers of a species of animal. Many fish, sea turtles, and birds are especially noted for their long migrations.

Mollusk: Any of a large group of soft-bodied, boneless animals, usually but not always protected by a shell. The group includes snails, clams, squid, and many other forms.

Molt: To shed or cast off a body covering, such as the shell-like external skeleton of a *crustacean* or the feathers of a bird.

Niche: An organism's role in a natural *community*, such as seed eater or *predator*. The term refers to the organism's function, not the place where it is found.

Oceanic island: An island that rose directly from the ocean floor without ever having been attached to a continental mainland. Most oceanic islands originated as *volcanoes*. *See also* Continental island.

Operculum: The horny or shell-like plate on the foot of a snail. It serves as a lid to seal the opening of the shell when the snail's body is retracted.

Pelagic: Living on or over the open sea, far from land.

Perennial: A plant that lives for several years and usually produces seeds each year.

Phytoplankton: Plant *plankton*.

Plankton: The minute plants and animals that float or swim near the surface of a body of water. The enormous quantities of plankton in seawater provide an important food source for many animals.

Polyp: An individual *coral* animal. Certain coral relatives, such as hydras and sea anemones, also are called polyps. Each polyp has a tubular or saclike body surmounted by a ring of fingerlike tentacles surrounding the mouth.

Predator: An animal that lives by capturing other animals for food.

Proboscis: A conspicuously long, flexible snout, as on elephants or elephant seals.

Reef: A narrow ridge of rocks or sand at or near the surface of a body of water.

Relict: A plant or animal *species* surviving on an *island* or in some other restricted geographical area long after its kind has become extinct elsewhere.

Reptile: A member of the group of animals including snakes, lizards, turtles, alligators, and others. Reptiles typically are *cold-blooded,* are covered by horny scales or plates, breathe by means of lungs, and lay eggs.

Scavenger: An animal that eats the dead remains and wastes of other animals and plants.

Snorkel: A curved tube, often attached to a face mask, used by a swimmer to breathe underwater.

Specialization: The sum of the *adaptations* that enable a plant or animal to survive in a particular *habitat* or equip it for a particular mode of life.

Species (singular or plural): A group of plants or animals whose members breed naturally only with each other and resemble each other more closely than they resemble members of any similar group.

Territory: An area defended by an animal against others of the same *species*. A territory may be used for breeding, feeding, or both.

Volcanic island: An island formed by the eruption of a submarine *volcano*.

Volcano: An opening in the earth's crust through which gases, ashes, and molten *lava* escape from the interior of the earth; a cone-shaped hill or mountain around such an opening, composed of material formerly expelled through the opening.

Warm-blooded: Able to maintain a fairly constant body temperature in spite of fluctuations in environmental temperature. Of all animals, only birds and *mammals* are warm-blooded. *See also* Cold-blooded.

Zoea: An early, free-swimming larval stage in the development of many *crustaceans*. *See also* Megalops.

Bibliography

ISLANDS AND ISLAND LIFE

BATES, MARSTON, and DONALD ABBOTT. *Coral Island*. Scribners, 1958.

BEEBE, WILLIAM. *Galápagos, World's End*. Putnam, 1924.

CARLQUIST, SHERWIN. *Island Life*. Natural History Press, 1965.

EIBL-EIBESFELDT, IRENAUS. *Land of a Thousand Atolls*. World, 1967.

EIBL-EIBESFELDT, IRENAUS. *The Galápagos, Noah's Ark of the Pacific*. Doubleday, 1961.

KEAST, ALLEN. *Australia and the Pacific Islands*. Random House, 1966.

KLINGEL, GILBERT C. *The Ocean Island*. Doubleday, 1961.

NELSON, BRYAN. *Galápagos, Islands of Birds*. Morrow, 1968.

RUSSELL, FRANKLIN. *The Secret Islands*. Norton, 1966.

WALLACE, ALFRED RUSSELL. *Island Life*. Macmillan, 1880.

WENKAM, ROBERT. *Kauai and The Park Country of Hawaii*. Sierra Club, 1965.

ECOLOGY

AMOS, WILLIAM H. *The Life of the Seashore*. McGraw-Hill, 1966.

BERRILL, N. J. *The Life of the Ocean*. McGraw-Hill, 1966.

DARLINGTON, PHILIP J. *Zoogeography*. Wiley, 1957.

ELTON, CHARLES S. *The Ecology of Invasions by Animals and Plants*. Wiley, 1958.

FARB, PETER, and THE EDITORS OF LIFE. *Ecology*. Time Inc., 1963.

MOORE, HILARY B. *Marine Ecology*. Wiley, 1958.

RIDLEY, HENRY N. *The Dispersal of Plants Throughout the World*. L. Reeve, 1930.

EVOLUTION

COLBERT, EDWIN H. *Evolution of the Vertebrates*. Wiley, 1955.

DARWIN, CHARLES. *On the Origin of Species, a Facsimile of the First Edition*. Atheneum, 1967.

LACK, DAVID. *Darwin's Finches*. Harper, 1961.

MOORE, RUTH, and THE EDITORS OF LIFE. *Evolution*. Time Inc., 1962.

SIMPSON, GEORGE GAYLORD. *The Major Features of Evolution*. Columbia University Press, 1953.

BIRDS

ALEXANDER, W. B. *Birds of the Ocean*. Putnam, 1928.

ECKERT, ALLAN. *The Great Auk*. Little, Brown, 1963.

FISHER, JAMES. *The Fulmar*. Collins, 1952.

FISHER, J., and R. M. LOCKLEY. *Sea-Birds*. Houghton Mifflin, 1954.

LOCKLEY, R. M. *Puffins*. Devin-Adair, 1953.

LOCKLEY, R. M. *Shearwaters*. Devin-Adair, 1942.

MAYR, ERNST. *Birds of the Southwest Pacific*. Macmillan, 1945.

MUNRO, GEORGE C. *Birds of Hawaii*. Ridgeway Press, 1960.

MURPHY, ROBERT CUSHMAN. *Oceanic Birds of South America*. American Museum of Natural History, 1936.

PALMER, RALPH S. (Editor). *Handbook of North American Birds* (Vol. I). Yale University Press, 1962.

PETERSON, ROGER TORY, and THE EDITORS OF LIFE. *The Birds*. Time Inc., 1963.

SPARKS, JOHN, and TONY SOPER. *Penguins*. Taplinger, 1967.

WATSON, GEORGE E. *Seabirds of the Tropical Atlantic Ocean*. Smithsonian, 1966.

OTHER ANIMALS

ABBOTT, R. TUCKER. *Sea Shells of the World*. Golden Press, 1962.

ABBOTT, R. TUCKER. *Seashells of North America*. Golden Press, 1968.

CARR, ARCHIE. *So Excellent a Fishe*. Natural History Press, 1967.

CARSON, RACHEL. *The Edge of the Sea*. Houghton Mifflin, 1955.

FISHER, JAMES, NOEL SIMON, and JACK VINCENT. *Wildlife in Danger*. Viking, 1969.

MAXWELL, GAVIN. *Seals of the World*. Houghton Mifflin, 1968.

MORRIS, PERCY A. *A Field Guide to Shells of the Pacific Coast and Hawaii*. Houghton Mifflin, 1966.

SCHEFFER, VICTOR B. *Seals, Sea Lions and Walruses*. Stanford University Press, 1958.

WARMKE, GERMAINE L., and R. TUCKER ABBOTT. *Caribbean Seashells*. Livingston, 1961.

EARTH SCIENCES

SHEPARD, FRANCIS P. *The Earth Beneath the Sea*. Johns Hopkins, 1967.

SMITH, F. G. W. *Atlantic Coral Reefs*. University of Miami Press, 1948.

THORARINSSON, SIGURDUR. *Surtsey, The New Island in the North Atlantic*. Viking, 1967.

WILCOXSON, KENT. *Chains of Fire: The Story of Volcanoes*. Chilton, 1966.

Illustration Credits and Acknowledgments

COVER: Blue-footed boobies, Thase Daniel

ENDPAPERS: Hanseki Yoshida, Freelance Photographers Guild.

UNCAPTIONED PHOTOGRAPHS: 8–9: Bird Rock, Steve and Dolores McCutcheon 64–65: Galápagos, David Cavagnaro 130–131: Swimming sea lions, Chuck Nicklin

ALL OTHER ILLUSTRATIONS: 10–11: David Cavagnaro 12: M. F. Soper 13: Donald S. Heintzelman 14–15: Sven Gillsater, Bruce Coleman Limited 16: Donald S. Heintzelman 17–18: Camera Press–Pix 19: Hans Zillessen, G.A.I. 20–21: Jack Fields; Keith Gillett 22: Matilda Metcalf 23: Douglas Faulkner 24: Ron Church 25: Douglas Faulkner; Bill Slosky 26: Hans Zillessen, G.A.I. 27: United States Department of the Interior 28–29: M. Woodbridge Williams, National Park Service 30–31: Zuber, Rapho Guillumette 32: Patricia C. Henrichs 33: Nick Drahos 34: Philippa Scott, Natural History Photographic Agency; M. Woodbridge Williams, National Park Service 35: Michael Berrill 36–37: Douglas Faulkner 38: Walter Dawn 39: Ernst S. Reese 40: Jack Dermid 41: Arabelle Wheatley 42–43: Ernst S. Reese 44: S. Arthur Reed 45: S. Arthur Reed; Ernst S. Reese 46–47: Karl Mayer 48–49: Nick Drahos 50: Karl Mayer 51: Arabelle Wheatley 52: David L. Pearson 53: Keith Gillett 54: Kelly Motherspaugh 56–57: Patricia C. Henrichs 58: Thase Daniel 60: Keith Gillett 61: Richard Mariscal 62: Tom Myers, Photo Researchers 66–67: Richard Mariscal 68–69: Graphic Arts International 70–71: Grant Haist 72: Tad Nichols 73: David Cavagnaro 74: Hans Zillessen, G.A.I. 75: Grant Haist 76: Thase Daniel 77: Richard Mariscal 78: Grant Haist 79: David Cavagnaro; Richard Mariscal 81: David Cavagnaro 82: Grant Haist 83–85: Richard Mariscal 86: Tad Nichols 87: Edmund Hobson 89: Tad Nichols 90: Patricia C. Henrichs 91: James Murray, Photo Researchers 92: Robert Bowman 93: Roger Tory Peterson, Photo Researchers 94–95: Arabelle Wheatley 96–97: Hans Zillessen, G.A.I. 98: Richard Mariscal 99: Grant Haist 101: Thase Daniel 102–103: Patricia C. Henrichs 104–105: Grant Haist 106: Howard Uible, Photo Researchers 107–108: Edward S. Ross 109–110: Howard Uible, Photo Researchers 111: Howard Uible, Photo Researchers; Edward S. Ross 112–113: Graphic Arts International 114: T. Stell Newman 116: Werner Stoy/Camera Hawaii 117: Hawaii Volcanoes National Park 118: James Larson; William Sager 119: Werner Stoy/Camera Hawaii 120: L. R. Owen 121: S. Arthur Reed 122–123: T. Stell Newman 124: Peter Sanchez 125: John Gerard 126–127: V. C. Betts, National Park Service 128: Ray Atkeson 132–133: Lois and Louis Darling 134: Patricia C. Henrichs 135: N. J. Berrill 136: Patricia C. Henrichs 137: Ian McLaren 138: E. R. Degginger 140–141: William J. Bolte 142–143: Fred Bruemmer 144–145: John Barlee 146: Keith Gillett 147: Fred Baldwin, Photo Researchers 148–149: Patricia C. Henrichs 150–151: Fred Bruemmer 153: Ruth Smiley 154: Arabelle Wheatley 155: David Cavagnaro 156: Richard Mariscal 157: Tad Nichols 158: Richard Mariscal 161: M. F. Soper 162: Arabelle Wheatley 163–166: W. L. N. Tickell 168–169: Arabelle Wheatley 170–171: Steve and Dolores McCutcheon 172: John Warham 174–175: Cordell Hicks 176: W. L. N. Tickell 177: Hans Zillessen, G.A.I. 178: Tom McHugh, Photo Researchers 180: National Park Service 182: University of California at Santa Cruz; National Park Service 183: National Park Service 184–185: Camera Press–Pix 186–187: Robert T. Orr 189: John Warham 190–192: Thase Daniel 193: Dr. Craig B. Kensler 195: H. Armstrong Roberts 196–197: Carrere, Rapho Guillumette 198: William J. Bolte 201: Patricia C. Henrichs 203–208: Charles Fracé 209–211: Patricia C. Henrichs (after Abbott) 212–213: Jeppesen and Company 214–216: Patricia C. Henrichs 217–221: Arabelle Wheatley

PHOTO EDITOR: BARBARA KNOWLTON

ACKNOWLEDGMENTS: *Although it is impossible to thank all those who assisted in preparation of this book, several people deserve special mention. The editors are especially grateful to Dean Amadon and Hobart Van Deusen of the American Museum of Natural History, both of whom reviewed the entire manuscript and offered many helpful suggestions, and to Ernst S. Reese of the University of Hawaii, who reviewed a portion of the manuscript. The editors would also like to give special thanks to C. Gordon Fredine, William L. Perry, and O. L. Wallis of the National Park Service for their cheerful cooperation and many useful suggestions.*

Index

[Page numbers in **boldface** type indicate reference to illustrations.]